TIME AND MODALITY

Oxford University Press, Amen House, London E.C.4

GLASGOW   NEW YORK   TORONTO   MELBOURNE   WELLINGTON

BOMBAY   CALCUTTA   MADRAS   KARACHI

CAPE TOWN   IBADAN   NAIROBI   ACCRA   SINGAPORE

TIME
AND MODALITY

*Being the John Locke Lectures for 1955–6
delivered in the University of Oxford*

BY

A. N. PRIOR

PROFESSOR OF PHILOSOPHY
CANTERBURY UNIVERSITY COLLEGE
NEW ZEALAND

OXFORD
AT THE CLARENDON PRESS
1957

PRINTED IN GREAT BRITAIN

To

MARY PRIOR

PREFACE

THESE lectures are the expression of a conviction that formal logic and general philosophy have more to bring to one another than is sometimes supposed. I do not mean by saying this to underrate the work of those who have explored the properties of symbolic calculi without any concern as to what they might be used to mean. On the contrary, I have drawn heavily upon their results (especially those of the late Professor McKinsey and his school); I have been glad to have given occasion for some further work of the same kind; and I have even (especially in Appendixes B and C) tried my hand at it a little myself. Nor do I mean to underrate what recent philosophers have done in the way of exploring the obstinate and intricate 'logic' embedded in common discourse, even when they have not derived or sought to derive anything like a calculus from it. I have my indebtednesses on this side too (I think here especially of some conversations with Professor Ryle during his New Zealand visit of 1954). But these two activities are, or can be, related to one another very much as theory and observation are in the physical sciences; and I must confess to a hankering after well-constructed theories which much contemporary philosophy fails to satisfy. Certainly we have a duty to notice that facts X and Y do not fit into such-and-such a formal logician's strait-jacket (it may be Aristotle's, or it may be Russell's or Quine's), but we should not neglect either to hunt for some better-fitting clothing for them, especially since the formal logician's shop is now so much more variously stocked. I am very conscious, though, that in the last two or three of these lectures, when I arrive at the most difficult reaches of my main subject, I have myself done little more than turn the ground over once or twice.

I should like to thank the University of Oxford for asking me to give these lectures; and Dr. Alan Ross Anderson of Yale and Mr E. J. Lemmon of Magdalen College, Oxford, for eliminating some errors. (I have also drawn a little upon the positive results of their investigations into the system Q; but only a little, as I hope they will make most of them known independently.) And while I differed radically from the late

Professor Łukasiewicz on the subject of modal logic, my debt to him will be obvious on almost every page.

A. N. P.

Oxford 1956

CONTENTS

I

Basic Modal Logic and the Ł-Modal System

THE general subject of these lectures is to be modal logic, and I shall be using a symbolism in which M stands for the weak modal operator which is usually read as 'Possibly' and L for the strong modal operator which is usually read as 'Necessarily'. I shall, however, be often using these two symbols in senses which are very remote from any ordinary senses of the words 'Possibly' and 'Necessarily'; and while I make no apology for this, something in the way of an explanation is perhaps in order.

Let me begin by citing a parallel case. We all know that there are a great many different kinds of statement which logicians have called implications or conditional statements. Any of these might be, and more than one of them has been, represented in notations of the Polish type by the form Cpq. There is, for example, two-valued truth-functional implication; various many-valued truth-functional implications; intuitionist implication; Lewis's various strict implications (I mean the strict implications defined by the postulate-sets of Lewis's systems S1 to S8); the tense-logical implications of Diodorus and Philo, referred to in the Middle Ages as the *consequentia simplex* and the *consequentia ut nunc*; and then there are sundry more obscure complexes going by the name of 'entailment'. When the letter C is being used for an implication operator, the contextual patter usually makes it clear *which* implication operator is intended in a given treatise, chapter, lecture, or paper; and where more than one is being discussed at once it is always possible to introduce other symbols, for example C' for strict implication or F for intuitionist implication. Recently the Chinese logician Moh Shaw-Kwei has attempted to lay down the conditions which entitle an operator to be considered as an implication-operator, and so to be represented by the symbol C, with or without various suffixes or other distinguishing adornments.[1] His conditions are extremely liberal; there is in

---

[1] Moh Shaw-Kwei, 'Logical Paradoxes for Many-valued Systems', *Journal of Symbolic Logic*, vol. xix (1954), pp. 37–40.

B

fact only one condition—that the rule of detachment, that if α and $C\alpha\beta$ are laws so is β a law, should hold. As he himself points out, not only ordinary implication-operators but equivalence operators count as implication-operators by this criterion. This is not as unheard-of as it might appear; there is good evidence, for example, that Boethius used the Latin 'si' to mean 'if and only if' as well as the plain 'if'.[1] But in any case it would be unreasonable to expect any precise definition of 'implication operator' to cover everything that ordinary speech would count as such, and nothing besides. It is a commonplace now that ordinary speech cannot be handled thus, that its words have 'families' of meanings, and that any single formula for their use will cover either too little or too much. It ought to be a commonplace also that this does not matter, and that for scientific purposes we draw our lines of demarcation not where custom dictates but where they will best facilitate generalization; and the common properties of Professor Moh's 'implication-operators' happen to be interesting.

Both in common speech and in the history of philosophy, the adverbs 'necessarily' and 'possibly' have been put to almost as many uses as the conjunction 'if', so that if I use the modal symbols L and M rather widely, I could cite precedents, and from time to time I shall do so. But further—and this is in the end a more important line of defence—a set of precise conditions for regarding a logical system as a 'modal' one, analogous to Moh Shaw-Kwei's definition of an implication-operator, has recently been laid down by Łukasiewicz,[2] and I shall not, to begin with at least, be straying beyond 'modal logic' in the sense which he gives to the term. If, later on, I work with a slightly more liberal sense of 'modal', I will offer some philosophical justification for doing so.

To count as a modal logic, according to Łukasiewicz, a system must contain a pair of one-argument operators forming statements out of statements, with the following properties: The more powerful modal operator, which we may symbolize as L, must be such that Lp is a stronger form than p, and yet not so

---

[1] See R. van den Driessche, 'Sur le *De Syllogismo Hypothetico* de Boèce', *Methodos*, vol. i (1949), pp. 293–307.

[2] J. Łukasiewicz, 'A System of Modal Logic', *Journal of Computing Systems*, vol. i, No. 3 (July 1953), § 1.

strong as to be never true. That is, 'If Lp then p', but not its converse, must be a logical law, and the simple NLp must not be one. And the feebler modal operator, which we may symbolize as M, must be such that Mp is a weaker, more non-committal form than p, and yet not so non-committal as to be never false. That is, 'If p then Mp', but not its converse, must be a logical law, and the simple Mp must not be one. Finally, Mp must be equivalent to $NLNp$ and Lp to $NMNp$. In the more liberal sense of 'modal' at which I have hinted above, the last pair of conditions is dropped. But even the more stringent conditions will be found on examination to be met by many systems which we would not ordinarily count as modal ones; but this is only to be expected, and is not to be regretted but welcomed. The aim of the definition is to be inclusive, and if this net catches more fish than it was primarily designed to catch, then from that very fact we have learnt something, and we have also provided ourselves with a means of saying what we have learnt.

As a matter of history, one of the strangest of the fish that this net has caught is the one which it *was* primarily designed by its maker to catch, the system which Łukasiewicz calls his Ł-modal one. Ever since this system was put forward in 1953 logicians, including Łukasiewicz himself, have been finding new oddities in it.[1] Here is one which I do not think has yet been mentioned: The schoolmen distinguished between what they called *necessitas consequentiae*, the necessity of the consequence or implication as a whole, and *necessitas consequentis*, the necessity of the consequent or implied proposition. For example, the statement 'If someone is a logician then necessarily someone is a logician' is true if it means 'It is necessary that if someone is a logician then someone is a logician', that is, if it asserts a *necessitas consequentiae*; but it is false if it means 'If someone is a logician then it is necessary that someone is a logician', that is, if it asserts a *necessitas consequentis*. But one of the laws of the Ł-modal system is $CLCpqCpLq$, by which any assertion of the form 'It is necessary that if p then q' implies the corresponding assertion of the form 'If p then it is necessary that q'.

[1] J. Łukasiewicz, op. cit., § 9; 'Arithmetic and Modal Logic', *JCS*, vol. i, No. 4 (Dec. 1954); 'On a Controversial Problem of Aristotle's Modal Syllogistic', *Dominican Studies*, vol. vii (1954); I. Thomas, 'Note on a Modal System of Łukasiewicz', ibid., vol. vi (1953), pp. 167–70; Alan Ross Anderson, *JCS*, vol. i, No. 4, Paper 17; A. N. Prior, ibid., Paper 16.

There is, however, a way of looking at the Ł-modal system which makes these and other results seem entirely reasonable. The form 'Possibly p' has many meanings, but there is as it were an upper and a lower limit to what it may mean. It never asserts *more* than that p is actually true, and it never asserts *less* that that p is true if it is true. Similarly 'Necessarily p' never asserts less than that p is actually true, and never asserts more than that p is at once true and false (for this last is a kind of upper limit to all assertion—if you'd believe that you'd believe anything). In all modal systems except this one, it is assumed that these limits lie outside, even if just outside, the range of permissible meanings of 'Possibly' and 'Necessarily'. That is, 'Possibly p' is taken to assert not only not more than but definitely less than the plain p (being true in cases in which the plain p is not true) and not only not less than but definitely more than 'If p then p' (since this is true even for p's which would ordinarily be called not possible but *im*possible. It is true, for example, that if 2 and 2 both are and are not 4 then 2 and 2 both are and are not 4). But the formulae which occur in the Ł-modal system as axioms and theorems are not those which hold when 'possibly p' is given a meaning *between* the upper and lower limit, but those which hold *whether it be given the upper-limit meaning or the lower-limit meaning*. That is, in the formulae of this system the operator M behaves as if it were not a constant but a variable operator, capable of standing either for the plain 'It is the case that' or for 'If it is the case that (so-and-so) then it is'. $CpMp$, for example, is a law because it holds whether you replace Mp by the plain p or by Cpp; the converse $CMpp$ is not a law because it does not hold when you replace Mp by Cpp; and the simple Mp is not a law because it does not hold when you replace it by the plain p. The L of the Ł-modal system may be interpreted similarly—the theses of the system containing L are those formulae containing L which will be laws of the ordinary propositional calculus whether Lp be replaced by the plain p or by $KpNp$. The odd formula $CLCpqCpLq$ is a law because if you simply drop the L you obtain $CCpqCpq$, which is an obvious enough tautology, and if you replace $L\alpha$ by $K\alpha N\alpha$ it becomes $CKCpqNCpqCpKqNq$, which is always true because its antecedent is always false.

It is clearly possible to produce further calculi on these lines.

For example, we might introduce the symbol G as a variable two-valued truth-operator with its range restricted to

(i) 'It is or is not the case that',
(ii) 'It is the case that', and
(iii) 'It is not the case that';

and H as an abbreviation for NGN, which for the above values of G would take the following:

(i) 'It is and is not the case that',
(ii) 'It is the case that', and
(iii) 'It is not the case that'.

This would not yield a modal logic in the sense of Łukasiewicz, since we would not have either $CpGp$, $CGpp$, $CpHp$, or $CHpp$. We would, however, have $CHpGp$ (but not $CGpHp$) and $CHCpqCHp$-Hq, laws which would hold intuitively if G were read as 'possibly' and H as 'necessarily', and also if G were read as 'It is permissible that' and H as 'It is obligatory that'. We would, however, also have $CGCpqCGpGq$, which does not suit either of these interpretations (though we have $CMCpqCMpMq$ in the Ł-modal system also).

I do not know whether anyone has ever used the words 'Possibly' and 'Necessarily' in the way in which I am suggesting that the M and L of the Ł-modal system could be used. It would be rash to say that no one ever has, just as it would be rash and indeed definitely erroneous to say that no one has ever used 'if' to mean 'if and only if', or to express material implication. Sometimes when a man says 'Possibly p' it does look as if he is trying to convey to some people the idea that he is assenting to the proposition p, and to others that he is not really committing himself to anything at all, and I suppose this would be something like using 'Possibly' as a variable operator capable of taking these two values, and the Ł-modal calculus would serve to show what propositions such a man could assent to without giving the game away. But the remoter uses of this calculus do not matter; it is in any case an admirable device for investigating the common properties of the forms p and Cpp.[1] If a device for doing this is something quite unlike what anyone has ever

---

[1] For a similar investigation of the common properties of the forms Cpq and Epq, see H. Rasiowa, 'On a Fragment of the Implicative Propositional Calculus', *studia Logica* (Warsaw), vol. iii (1955).

meant before by a modal system, this only makes it all the more interesting that the system has in common with easily recognized modal systems the set of features listed by Łukasiewicz as the 'basic modal logic'.

On one ground, indeed, a doubt may be raised as to whether the Ł-modal logic, with this interpretation, really *has* this set of features. For are L and M, interpreted as above, really *statement-forming* operators on statements? Attach M to '2 and 2 and 5', for example, and what you obtain is not a statement but only something which becomes a statement when the variable M is given one of its two possible values. '$M(2+2=5)$' is not a statement but only the common form of the two statements '$2+2=5$' and 'If $2+2=5$ then $2+2=5$'. For such statement forms, however, the term 'open statement' is often used by contemporary logicians, so we could defend the 'modal' character of the Ł-modal system, with the suggested interpretation, by saying that its L and M at least form open statements out of statements. If, however, this extension of the notion of a statement is to be permitted when applying Łukasiewicz's definition of 'modal', we must also count the ordinary theory of quantification as a modal system; for the quantifiers Πx and Σx form statements out of open statements, and we assert as laws $C\phi x\Sigma x\phi x$ and $C\Pi x\phi x\phi x$, corresponding to $CpMp$ and $CLpp$, while rejecting $C\Sigma x\phi x\phi x$, $C\phi x\Pi x\phi x$, $\Sigma x\phi x$, and $N\Pi x\phi x$, corresponding to $CMpp$, $CpLp$, Mp, and NLp.

This conclusion would be entirely welcome to some logicians, for example von Wright,[1] who describes the quantifiers as 'existential modalities'. It would not, I suspect, be so welcome to Łukasiewicz;[2] and Łukasiewicz's own interpretation of his Ł-modal calculus is not the one I have suggested above either— for him, the 'necessarily' and 'possibly' of this calculus are not *variable two-valued* truth-operators, but *constant four-valued* ones. Łukasiewicz seems inclined to interpret all modal logics after the general pattern of his 3-valued logic of 1920, and he says explicitly that all modal logics, in his sense of the term, must be many-valued.[3] If we explicitly exclude, as possible interpretations of the L and M of his 'basic modal logic', operators which

---

[1] G. H. von Wright, *An Essay in Modal Logic* (1951), ch. i.
[2] Cf. his paper in the *Proceedings of the XIth Congress of Philosophy* (1953), xiv. 86.
[3] *JCS*, vol. i, No. 3, p. 113.

either form open statements out of closed ones or closed ones out of open ones, we must agree with him both that ordinary quantification theory is not a modal logic, and that if we take a modal logic to be truth-functional at all, it must be many-valued.

The first point is obvious, and the second can be quite simply proved. In a two-valued truth-functional system, there are four and only four types of statement-forming operators on single statements (open statements being excluded)—the sort, call it V, which forms true statements out of both true and false ones; the sort, call it S, which forms a function of the same value as its argument; the sort, call it N, which forms a function of the opposite value to its argument; and the sort, call it F, which forms false statements from both true and false ones. And as Łukasiewicz points out, none of these will do for his L and M. With V, the tautology-forming operator, we have Vp as a law, and this does not suit either L or M; with S, 'It is the case that', we have both $CSpp$ and $CpSp$ as laws, and this does not suit L or M, each of which has one of these only; with N, we have neither $CNpp$ nor $CpNp$ as a law, and this does not suit L or M, each of which has at least one of these; with F, the contradiction-forming operator, we have NFp as a law, and this does not suit L or M. It can also be shown, conversely, that all truth-functional logics with more values than 2 are modal, at least if they contain symbols for all possible functions with the number of values in question. For 3-valued logic contains a pair of operators with the required properties, and it has been shown by Tzu-Hua Hoo[1] that in any $m+1$-valued logic we can construct a model of the corresponding m-valued logic, i.e. we can always find $m+1$-valued operators with the same formal properties as the m-valued operators.

But need we consider modal logics as being truth-functional at all? I certainly do not think this is necessary, nor do I know whether it is in all cases possible, but very often at least, the treatment of modal logics as many-valued truth-functional systems, with the notion of a 'truth-value' enlarged a little, does provide us with an extremely fruitful instrument of inquiry. I cannot establish this point immediately, but it is one which I shall be illustrating in detail in what follows.

[1] 'm-valued sub-system of $(m+n)$-valued propositional calculus', *Journal of Symbolic Logic*, vol. xiv (1949), pp. 177–81.

II

Tense-logic and an Analogue of S4

In the next few lectures I shall be concentrating on a kind of logic, the logic of tenses, which is almost as far removed as Łukasiewicz's Ł-modal system, or the theory of quantification, from what we ordinarily understand by modal logic. I shall show, however, that this *is* a modal logic in the sense of Łukasiewicz, and even that it is structurally very similar to systems which we have no hesitation in classifying as modal; and that it can also be represented, and for some purposes is worth representing, as a many-valued system.

In the logic of tenses, the ordinary statement-variables p, q, r, etc., are used to stand for statements in what is not now the ordinary sense of the term 'statement', though it was the ordinary sense in ancient and medieval logic. They are used to stand for 'statements' in the sense in which the truth-value of a statement may be different at different times—the sense in which, for example, 'It is summer in England' would count as a statement, and in which it would be said that this statement is now false but will be true in a few months' time. And I shall, to begin with, employ the symbols P and F to mean respectively 'It has been the case that' and 'It will be the case that'. A little should be said about the exact force of these two operators. The statement 'It will be the case that Professor Carnap is flying to the moon', as I understand it, is not a statement *about* the statement 'Professor Carnap is flying to the moon', but a new statement about Professor Carnap, formed from the simpler one by means of the operator F. It is exactly equivalent to the colloquial form 'Professor Carnap will be flying to the moon', which is quite obviously a statement about Professor Carnap, and quite obviously not a statement about the statement 'Professor Carnap is flying to the moon'. The function of the operator F, in short, is that of forming a future-tense statement from the corresponding present-tense one, and the future-tense statement is not about the present-tense one, but is about whatever the present-tense statement is about. The same remarks apply, *mutatis mutandis*, to the operator 'It has been the case that', and in my view they apply also to the operators 'It could be that' and 'I think that'. 'It has been the case that Professor Carnap is flying to the moon', 'It could be that Professor Carnap is flying to the moon', and 'I think that Professor Carnap is flying to the moon' are all of them statements about Professor Carnap, not statements about the statement 'Professor Carnap is flying to the moon'.

But although the statement 'It will be the case that Professor Carnap is flying to the moon', that is, 'Professor Carnap will be flying to the moon', is not exactly a statement *about* the statement 'Professor Carnap is flying to the moon', we may say that the future-tense statement *is* true if and only if the present-tense statement *will be* true. Similarly the past-tense statement 'It has been the case that Professor Carnap is flying to the moon', that is, 'Professor Carnap has been flying to the moon', *is* true if and only if the present-tense statement 'Professor Carnap is flying to the moon' *has been* true; the modal statement 'It could be that Professor Carnap is flying to the moon' *is* true if and only if the assertoric statement 'Professor Carnap is flying to the moon' *could be* true, and the statement 'It is believed that Professor Carnap is on his way to the moon' *is* true if and only if the simple statement 'Professor Carnap is on his way to the moon' *is believed to be* true. Semantic rules of this sort were stated by the schoolmen, and they are after all very simple and obvious.[1] Similar rules may be stated for compounded and iterated operators. For example, the statement 'It will be the case that it will be the case that Professor Carnap is flying to the moon' *is* true if and only if the statement 'It will be the case that Professor Carnap is flying to the moon' *will be* true; and the statement 'It will be the case that it has been the case that Professor Carnap is flying to the moon', or more colloquially 'Professor Carnap will have been flying to the moon' *is* true if and only if the past-tense statement 'Professor Carnap has been flying to the moon' *will be* true.

It would be possible to introduce into our system also the present-tense operator 'It is the case that', but it is not difficult to see that this is a superfluous complication. For the statement 'It is the case that Professor Carnap is flying to the moon' *is* true

[1] See Moody, *Truth and Consequence in Medieval Logic* (1953), pp. 53–54.

if and only if the statement 'Professor Carnap is flying to the moon' *is* true, and *will be* true if and only if the simple statement *will be* true, and *has been* true if and only if the simple statement *has been* true. Or to put the point more metaphysically, the *presence of the presence* of an event or state is simultaneous with the *presence* of that event or state, and that in turn is simultaneous with the event or state itself; the *futurity of the presence* of an event or state is simultaneous with the *futurity* of the event or state itself, and so is the *presence of the futurity* of the event or state; and the *pastness of the presence* of an event or state is simultaneous with the *pastness* of the event or state itself, and so is the *presence of the pastness* of the event or state. Using 'S' for 'It is the case that', we may represent these truths symbolically by the equations $SSp = Sp = p$, $SFp = FSp = Fp$, and $SPp = PSp = Pp$.

The idea that it is *necessary* to introduce a special present-tense operator would, moreover, have extremely awkward formal consequences. For to say that such an operator is necessary is to say that the expressions to which we attach it would not be propositions, at all events not tensed propositions, without it. This in turn is to say that tense-operators do not form propositions out of propositions, at all events out of tensed propositions; rather, they form propositions out of merely juxtaposed nouns and verbs, or they form tensed propositions out of untensed ones. And from this in turn it would follow that tense-operators cannot be iterated or attached to propositions to which tense-operators are already attached; that is, we would have to rule out such forms as 'It will be the case that it has been the case that p'. And to rule this would be practically to destroy tense-logic before we have started to build it.

I shall also be using the ordinary operators for constructing truth-functions, in the Łukasiewicz notation—N for 'It is not the case that'; K for 'and'; A for the non-exclusive 'or'; C for 'if', that is, for material implication; and E for 'if and only if', that is, for material equivalence. Such forms as Np and Kpq are, like the simpler forms entering into them, liable to have different truth-values at different times. Np is true at all times at which p is false, and false at all times at which p is true; Kpq is true at all times at which p and q are both true, and false at all other times; and the other truth-operators can be defined in terms of N and K in the usual way. As an example of Kpq, we may take 'It has been raining and it will be snowing'. This is true at all those times, and only those times, at which 'It has been raining' and 'It will be snowing' are both true; that is, at all those times, and only those times, at which 'It is raining' has been true and 'It is snowing' will be true. The question as to what is the tense of a form such as this, and as to whether it has any tense, seems to me a purely verbal one. There is no word in English, or so far as I know in any other language, for the tense of such a form; but we could invent a word for it if we wanted to, and in any case its truth-conditions are perfectly clear. And it has a tense, or is a tensed form, if by that we mean that a reference must be made to time in stating its truth-conditions; the question as to whether it has a tense in any other sense can only be answered when that other sense is explained.

Even the operator N introduces tense-distinctions over and above the simple ones with which we began. NFp, 'It will not be the case that p', is no doubt a future tense of some sort, but it is not the same as 'It will be the case that not p', FNp. If it were, then $NFNp$, 'It will not be the case that not p' would be the same as $FNNp$, and so the same as the simple Fp, 'It will be the case that p'. But in fact, 'It will not be the case that not p' is a stronger form than 'It will be the case that p'; it means something more like 'It will always be the case that p'. Similarly $NPNp$, 'It has not been the case that not p', is a stronger form than the simple Pp, 'It has been the case that p', and means something more like 'It has always been the case that p'.

These differences can perhaps be brought out more clearly if we modify our symbolism a little. So far we have used P and F as simply monadic statement-forming operators on statements. We may also use them, however, in a different way—as dyadic statement-forming operators for which the first argument is the measure of a time-interval and the second a statement. Using P in this sense, the form Pnp will mean 'It was the case n days ago that p' (if we use days as our time-unit). $P1p$, for example, will mean 'It was the case this time yesterday that p'. Fnp will similarly mean 'It will be the case n days hence'; for example $F1p$ means 'It will be the case this time tomorrow that p'. Our previous P and F can be defined in terms of the new P and F by means of the existential quantifier—'It will be the case that p' is now 'For some n, it will be the case n days hence that p', $\Sigma nFnp$, and our original Pp is similarly $\Sigma nPnp$. 'It will not be the case that not p' will now be analysed as 'There is no n such that it will be the case n days hence that not p', $N\Sigma nFnNp$; and this is almost the same as 'It will always be the case that p', or 'For all n, it will be the case n days hence that p', $\Pi nFnp$. Ordinary quantification theory, in which Πx is equivalent to $N\Sigma xN$, guarantees the equivalence of this last form $\Pi nFnp$ to $N\Sigma nNFnp$, 'There is no n such that it will not be the case n days hence that p'. Whether the form $N\Sigma nFnNp$, 'There is no n such that it will be the case n days hence that not p', is equivalent to this, depends on whether the form

'It will not be the case n days hence that p'

is equivalent to the form

'It will be the case n days hence that not p';

that is, on whether $NFnp$ is equivalent to $FnNp$. We shall find reasons later for questioning this equivalence, but they are a little recondite, and in the meantime we shall assume it to hold, and construct what systems we can on that assumption.

I shall now show that tense-logic as I have described it is a modal system, and that if we define M (or 'Possibly') as 'It either is or will be the case that', and L (or 'Necessarily') as 'It is and always will be the case that', these operators will meet Łukasiewicz's conditions for being modal operators and, furthermore, will have all the formal properties of the M and L of the Lewis system S4. 'Possibly' and 'Necessarily' were used in this sense by the Megarian logician Diodorus, and I have pointed out the resemblance between Diodoran modal logic and S4 elsewhere;[1] but I want now to prove this point more rigorously, and in a slightly different way. Of the tense-logic I have described, we need only use that part which contains the operator F, and I shall modify this part slightly by admitting as a special case of the form Fnp the form Fop, 'It will be the case no time-units hence that p'. This form is of course equivalent to

---

[1] A. N. Prior, 'Diodoran Modalities', *Philosophical Quarterly*, July 1955, Part I.

the simple p, and its implying p will be one of my axioms. The following is the full set of postulates that I wish to use:

Definitions:[1] Df. L: $Lp = \Pi nFnp$

Df. M: $Mp = \Sigma nFnp$

Rules: Substitution, detachment, Łukasiewicz's rules Π1, Π2, Σ1, and Σ2 for introducing quantifiers, and the special rule

RF: If α is a law, so is $Fn\alpha$.

Axioms: Any complete set of axioms for the classical propositional calculus, together with

1. $CFnNpNF\bar{n}p$
2. $CNF\bar{n}pFnNp$
3. $CFnCpqCFnpFnq$
4. $CFopp$
5. $CFmFnpFSmnp$
6. $CFm\Sigma nFnp\Sigma nFmFnp$

In axiom 5, the operator S is a time-forming operator on times, such that the interval Smn may be thought of as the sum of the intervals m and n. Axiom 5 therefore asserts that if it will be the case m days hence that it will be the case n days hence that p, then it will be the case $m+n$ days hence that p. The other axioms will, I think, sound reasonable if they are read off literally; any doubts we may have about axiom 2 we have agreed to waive in the meantime. The definitions of L and M are the Diodoran ones—'is and always will be' and 'is or will be', the 'is' case being included under the general form Fn as Fo.

---

[1] The application of these definitions, and of similar ones in later chapters, is subject to restrictions similar to those which must be imposed on ordinary substitution for variables in formulae containing quantifiers. Neither definitional substitution nor substitution for variables may be employed in cases in which it would turn a bound variable into a free one or vice versa, so we cannot replace ΣnFn by M or vice versa, or ΠnFn by L or vice versa, if the formula following contains a free n. (For example, $\Sigma nFnK\alpha Fn\beta$ is not to be equated with $MK\alpha Fn\beta$.) What this restriction amounts to is that M is an abbreviation for ΣnFn, not for $\Sigma nFn \ldots n \ldots$, and similarly with L. It does not affect any of the proofs used here, since these appeal to laws which have no free n in the 'governed' formulae, and to which the definitions are therefore applicable.

The following are among the theorems provable in the system:

7. $CMpNLNp$ ($C\Sigma nFnpN\Pi nNFnp$ by quantification theory; and $CN\Pi nNFnpN\Pi nFnNp$ by transposition from $C\Pi nFnNp\Pi nNFnp$, this coming from axiom 1 by $\Pi 1$ and $\Pi 2$).

8. $CNLNpMp$ (similarly from axiom 2).

9. $CLpp$ ($C\Pi nFnpFop$ by quantification theory, and $C\Pi nFnpp$ from this by axiom 4 and syllogism).

10. $CLCpqCLpLq$ (by axiom 3 and quantification theory).

11. $CLpLLp$ ($C\Sigma mnFmFnp\Sigma nFnp$ from 5 by quantification theory; $C\Sigma mFm\Sigma nFnp\Sigma nFnp$ from this by 6 and quantification theory; $C\Sigma nFn\Sigma nFnp\Sigma nFnp$, or $CMMpMp$, from this by quantification theory; and $CLpLLp$ from this by the usual transpositions, etc.).

And we may prove the following derivative rules:

12. If α is a theorem, so is $L\alpha$ (RF and the universalization rule of quantification theory, derivable from $\Pi 2$).

13. If $C\alpha\beta$ is a theorem, so is $CFn\alpha Fn\beta$ (RF and axiom 3).

Rule 13 is all that we need, over and above propositional calculus and quantification theory, to show that if α and β logically imply one another, they are mutually replaceable in any formula of the system. This gives the mutual implications 7 and 8 the force of a definition of M as NLN. And Gödel has shown that we have a modal system equivalent to Lewis's S4 if we have this definition, the classical propositional calculus, the laws 9, 10, and 11 and the rule 12.[1] S4 is of course a modal system in the sense that $CLpp$ and $CpMp$ are provable in it, while $CMpp$, $CpLp$, Mp, and NLp are not. That Mp and NLp are not provable is easily shown from the fact that there are theorems of the forms $NM\alpha$ and $L\alpha$, and the system is consistent. If we wish to express the non-derivability of $CMpp$ and $CpLp$ as formal

[1] K. Gödel, 'Eine Interpretation des intuitionistischen Aussagenkalküls', *Ergebnisse eines matematischen Kolloquiums*, vol. iv (1933), pp. 39–40; cited in R. Feys, 'Les systèmes formalisés des modalités aristotéliciennes', *Revue Philosophique de Louvain*, Nov. 1950, 16.1–16.24, and B. Sobociński, 'Note on a Modal System of Feys–von Wright', *Journal of Computing Systems*, vol. i, No. 3 (1953), pp. 171–2.

rejections, in the manner of Łukasiewicz, we may easily deduce these two rejections in our system if we add to our postulates Łukasiewicz's rules of rejection and the axiomatic rejection either of $CpFnp$ or of $CFnpp$.

This, then, is a modal logic; and it can be represented as a many-valued logic too. I shall not at present give this many-valued representation, which is one involving an infinite number of truth-values; but I shall take you a step or two on the way towards it. Let us suppose that there are only two times, today and tomorrow. Then we can assign to any statement one of the following four values, which are 'truth-values' of a sort: (1) true both today and tomorrow; (2) true today and false tomorrow; (3) false today and true tomorrow; and (4) false both today and tomorrow. It is clear that if p is true both today and tomorrow, Np is false both today and tomorrow, i.e. $N1 = 4$; and in general $Np = 5-p$. Again, if p is true both today and tomorrow, and q true today but not tomorrow, the conjunction 'Both p and q' will be true today but not tomorrow, i.e. $K12 = 2$. If p is true today but not tomorrow, and q true tomorrow but not today, the conjunction 'Both p and q' will not be true on either day, i.e. $K23 = 4$. Common sense easily suggests the rest of the table for K. If we use Mp for the assertion that it either is or will be the case that p, this will be true on both days if p is true on both days, i.e. $M1 = 1$; if p is true today but not tomorrow, the assertion that it either is or will be the case is also true today but not tomorrow, i.e. $M2 = 2$; if p is not true today but will be tomorrow, the assertion that it either is or will be true is true on both days, i.e. $M3 = 1$; if p is false on both days, so is Mp. In working out the table for Lp, 'It is and always will be the case that p', we count this as true tomorrow if p is true tomorrow—if p is true tomorrow, it is true for all the time that then remains. Without going further into particular cases, the tables for K, N, M, and L work out as follows:

K	1	2	3	4	N	M	L
*1	1	2	3	4	4	1	1
2	2	2	4	4	3	2	4
3	3	4	3	4	2	1	3
4	4	4	4	4	1	4	4

The table for Cpq, 'Not both p and not q', works out by calculation from the tables for N and K as follows:

C	1	2	3	4
*1	1	2	3	4
2	1	1	3	3
3	1	2	1	2
4	1	1	1	1

The value 1 is 'designated'; that is, we consider a formula to be verified by the tables if it has the value 1—true both times—for all possible values of its variables. For example, $CMMpMp$ is verified thus:

$$CMM1M1 = CM11 = C11 = 1$$
$$CMM2M2 = CM22 = C22 = 1$$
$$CMM3M3 = CM11 = C11 = 1$$
$$CMM4M4 = CM44 = C44 = 1$$

This is something like the many-valued logic we are after, but not quite; for our tables verify, beside our theorems 7–11 and the rule 12, a number of odd formulae which simply reflect our initial fiction that there are no times but today and tomorrow, for example the law $CKMKpqMKpNqLp$, 'If p either is or will be true both in conjunction with q and in conjunction with not-q then it neither is nor will be false'. If there really were only two times this would be reasonable, since q and not-q are never true on the same day, so if p is true in conjunction with each of them this must occur at different times, and so p must be true at the only two times there are. In an 8-valued logic allowing for three times, say yesterday, today, and tomorrow, such formulae as this would cease to be verified, but there would still be laws reflecting the fiction that the number of times is not more than three.[1] It is the matrix with an infinity of values towards which this series of finite matrices is tending which we really require. That alone will exclude all these odd formulae, and leave us only with the formulae of S4. But the 4-valued starting-point of the series is useful negatively, since whatever does *not*

[1] Cf. my 'Many-valued and Modal Systems: An Intuitive Approach', *Philosophical Review*, Oct. 1955.

hold in this 4-valued logic will not hold in S4 either. For example, the tables do not verify the formula $CMpLMp$, since $CM2LM2 = C2L2 = C24 = 3$. Nor would we want them to, with the tense-logical interpretation we have suggested for such formulae; for with this interpretation $CMpLMp$ would assert that whatever is or will be true is *and always will be* true or going to be true, and this is plainly false when p describes a process which has not yet, but some day will, stop for good. (The case for for which the tables falsify it is precisely the case corresponding to this one—the case in which p is true today but will not be tomorrow.)

This formula $CMpLMp$, though not a theorem of S4, is provable in the stronger Lewis system S5; and the 4-valued tables we have been interpreting are the standard ones used[1] for verifying S4 without verifying S5, thereby showing that the distinctive S5 laws are not provable in S4. S5 also, however, has an analogue within tense-logic, and along with it a many-valued representation.

[1] In Lewis and Langford, *Symbolic Logic* (1932), appendix ii.

III

A Tense-logical Analogue of S5

THE tense-logical analogue of S5 can be best approached by introducing the notion of associating an event with a *date*. This can be defined in terms of the operators already at our disposal —*Fn* now reverting to its original status as a purely future-tense operator, i.e. with the value *Fo* not admitted—together with a propositional constant of a particular sort. But first it will be as well to make clear a small point about the semantics of the operators *Pn* and *Fn*.

These operators may be prefixed to one another to form complex tenses, just as our original *P* and *F* could. We could have, for example, the form *PnFmp*. This may be literally rendered as 'It was the case *n* days ago that it will be the case *m* days hence that *p*'. We never talk quite like this in English, and if we did it would not be clear whether the '*m* days hence' would mean *m* days forward from the time of utterance or *m* days forward from the *n* days ago referred to in the first prefix. Here we shall use such forms quite definitely in the second sense. Our general rule is this: 'It was the case *n* days ago that *p* *is* true if and only if *p* itself *was* true *n* days ago. Hence the statement 'It was the case *n* days ago that it will be the case *m* days hence that *p*' is true if and only if the statement 'It will be the case *m* days hence that *p*' *was* true *n* days ago. To express a statement with these truth-conditions in ordinary English we would probably use some such form as 'It was the case *n* days ago that it *would* be the case *m* days later that *p*', but this is what we politely call an 'idiom' and the French more accurately an *idiotisme*, and we shall generally translate the symbols literally. Similarly, we shall use the form 'It was the case *n* days ago that it was the case *m* days ago that *p*' for what in ordinary English would be something more like 'It was the case *n* days ago that it *had been* the case *m* days before that *p*'; and the form 'It was the case *n* days ago that *x* is *ϕ*-ing' for what we would ordinarily say as 'It was the case *n* days ago that *x was ϕ*-ing'. (Logically, the common forms are on a level with 'I haven't seen nothing' for 'I have seen nothing'.)

And now for dates. All talk about dates involves a reference to some standard event which is presumed to be unique—the birth of Christ, the founding of Rome, the big wind, or whatever it might be. Let us use the symbol χ for the statement that this even is occurring, and let us use the form Tp to mean 'It either is or has been or will be the case that p', i.e. $AA(p)(\Sigma nPnp)(\Sigma nFnp)$. 'The date of p's occurrence is plus t' will then mean 'It either is or has been or will be the case that both (1) p, and (2) it was the case t time-units ago that χ', or in symbols, $TKpPt\chi$; 'The date of p's occurrence is minus t' will mean the same with P replaced by F, $TKpFt\chi$; and 'The date of p's occurrence is zero' will mean 'It either is or has been or will be the case that both p and χ', $TKp\chi$. In this way we associate the being-the-case of p with a number which is independent of the time at which we talk about it, though the complete tenselessness which some logicians attribute to dated statements seems to be illusory. What we have in these cases is a complex constructed entirely out of tensed statements, though in a slightly peculiar way; and if dated statements do not have different truth-values at different times, we shall later find reason for believing that they sometimes suffer in time an even worse fate than that.

Given the foregoing definitions, for positive, negative, and zero values of t, of 'The date of p's occurrence is t', or more briefly 'p at t', we can introduce for this form the symbol-sequence Utp. And we may now give new definitions to the modal operators M and L, namely 'at some time' and 'at all times', or symbolically,

$$\text{Df. } M: Mp = \Sigma t Utp$$
$$\text{Df. } L: Lp = \Pi t Utp$$

For this part of tense-logic we may lay down the following postulate-set, beside the above two definitions:

Rules. Substitution, detachment, Łukasiewicz's rules $\Pi 1$, $\Pi 2$, $\Sigma 1$ and $\Sigma 2$ for introducing quantifiers, and the special rule RU: If α is a law, so is $Ut\alpha$.

Axioms. Any set sufficient for the classical propositional calculus, together with the following:

1. $CUtNpNUtp$
2. $CNUtpUtNp$

3. *CUtCpqCUtpUtq*
4. *CΠtUtpp*
5. *CUt′UtpUtp*

This is a modification of a set used by Professor Łoś,[1] who originated the *Utp* notation. The definition of *Utp* will turn these special postulates into three sets (corresponding to the definitions for the three types of value for *t*) containing more or less complex *Pn-Fn* formulae, and I suspect that they would all be derivable from some much simpler set of *Pn-Fn* postulates. However, we are less concerned now with what they might be derivable from than with what they entail; and their consequences include the following theorems:

6. *CMpNLNp* (proved from 1, in the same manner as for our previous *M*).
7. *CNLNpMp* (ditto from 2).
8. *CLpp* (from 4 and Df. *L*).
9. *CLCpqCLpLq* (proved from 3, in the same manner as for our previous *M*).
10. *CNLpLNLp* (*CΠtUtpUtp* by quantification theory; *CUt′ ΠtUtpUt′Utp* from this by RU and 3; *CUt′ΠtUtpUtp* from this by 5; *CΣt′Ut′ΠtUtpΠtUtp* from this by quantification theory; *CMLpLp* from this by more quantification theory and Dff. *M* and *L*; and *CNLpLNLp* from this by the usual transpositions).

And the following derivative rules:

11. If α is a law, so is *Lα* (as for our previous *L*).
12. If *Cαβ* is a law, so is *CUtαUtβ* (as for *Fn*).

6, 7, and 12 have the same joint logical force as the definition of *M* as *NLN*; and Gödel[2] has shown that with this definition, the rule 11, and 8, 9, and 10 as axioms, we have a system equivalent to Lewis's S5. And intuitively, typical S5 formulae such as *CNLpLNLp*, *CMLpLp*, and *CMpLMp* do not seem objectionable

[1] In a Polish paper reviewed by H. Hiż in the *Journal of Symbolic Logic*, vol. xvi (1951), pp. 58–59.
[2] Op. cit.

with these definitions of L and M. $CMLpLp$, for example, asserts that if it is true at some time that it is true at all times that p, then it is true at all times that p.

This modal fragment of tense-logic, like that considered in our last, can be given a many-valued interpretation; and this time we shall develop this interpretation more deliberately, as our aim will be to define the final system with an infinity of values with some precision. We can begin as before with a 4-valued system based intuitively on the fiction that there are only two times, today and tomorrow; but we shall not begin by calling these values 1, 2, 3, and 4, but will call them 11, 13, 31, and 33. Here 1 represents plain truth and 3 represents plain falsehood; the first numeral gives the proposition's truth-value today, in the plain sense of truth-value, and the second gives its truth-value tomorrow. To find the value of Np, we naturally replace 1 by 3 and 3 by 1 wherever they occur; that is, we have

$$N(xy) = (Nx)(Ny),$$

where the N's on the right-hand side have the ordinary 2-valued table ($N1 = 3$, $N3 = 1$). Similarly we have

$$K(xy)(x'y') = (Kxx')(Kyy'),$$

where the K's on the right have the ordinary 2-valued table for K ($K11 = 1$, $K13 = K31 = K33 = 3$). For example

$$K(13)(13) = (K11)(K33) = (13),$$

i.e. if p is true today and false tomorrow, and q likewise, their conjunction is true today and false tomorrow. On the other hand

$$K(31)(13) = (K31)(K13) = (33),$$

i.e. if p is false today and true tomorrow, and q true today and false tomorrow, their conjunction is false on both days. In effect, we work out the value of Kpq in the normal way for each day in turn. Mp, which asserts in effect that p is true on at least one of the two days, is itself true on both days if p is true on either or both, and false on both days if p is false on both days; i.e. $M11 = M13 = M31 = 11$, and $M33 = 33$. Lp, asserting in effect that p is true on both days, can be worked out in a similar way. Summing up, we have for K, N, M, and L the following tables:

K	11	13	31	33	N	M	L
*11	11	13	31	33	33	11	11
13	13	13	33	33	31	11	33
31	31	33	31	33	13	11	33
33	33	33	33	33	11	33	33

The value 11 is 'designated', i.e. it is the one a formula must always have if it is to be considered as expressing a logical law. Renumbering our values as 1, 2, 3, and 4, we obtain

K	1	2	3	4	N	M	L
*1	1	2	3	4	4	1	1
2	2	2	4	4	3	1	4
3	3	4	3	4	2	1	4
4	4	4	4	4	1	4	4

These are the same tables as before for K and N, with different ones for M and L, and are the standard tables for verifying Lewis's S5. As with the 4-valued tables verifying S4 these tables also verify other formulae which are not laws of the Lewis systems, and which merely reflect our fiction of two times only. For example, the law $CKMKpqMKpNqLp$, 'If p-and-q is some-times true, and p-and-not-q is sometimes true, then p is true always'; if there are only two times, this would have to be so, for q and not-q cannot be true at the same time, so that if p is true in conjunction with each it must be true at two different times, and so, according to our fiction, at all times.

Remove this fiction, but preserve the basic pattern, and we have a logic with an infinity of 'truth-values' the laws of which, for M, L, and the ordinary truth-functions, are exactly those of S5. This 'preservation of the basic pattern' can now be described quite exactly.[1] The truth-values can now be represented by *infinite* sequences of 1's and 3's (if you like, by non-terminating decimals containing those numbers only). The sequence for Np

[1] At this point, and similarly in Chapter V, I am much indebted to the instruction of Mr. W. W. Sawyer.

will be the sequence for p with 1's replaced by 3's and vice versa, and the sequence for Kpq will be given by the equation

$$K(xyz\ldots)(x'y'z'\ldots) = (Kxx')(Kyy')(Kzz')\ldots,$$

where the K's on the right have the ordinary 2-valued table. The sequence for Mp is the sequence containing 1's only so long as the sequence for p contains any 1's, and if the sequence for p is that with 3's only, so is the sequence for Mp. Interchange 1's and 3's in this description of the conditions for M, and you have the conditions for L. The designated sequence is that containing 1's only.

The infinite matrix which is similarly characteristic for S4, and so for the fragment of tense-logic discussed previously, has the values of N and K determined in the same way, but those for M and L determined differently. The sequence for Mp has 1's going out as far as there are any 1's in the sequence for p, and if there is any place in the sequence for p such that there are only 3's from that point onwards, the sequence for Mp also has 3's from that point onwards. For example, if the sequence for p goes like this:

1311333333133133 (and only 3's after this)

the sequence for Mp goes like this:

1111111111111133 (and only 3's hereafter).

If you remember that Mp here means 'It is or will be the case that p', and suppose that in these sequences each place represents a time future to the one to the left of it, the rationale of this method of determination will be obvious. Interchange 1's and 3's in our description of the conditions for M, and you again have the conditions for L; and the designated sequence is again that containing 1's only.

Yet another 'modal' fragment of tense-logic is obtainable if we suppose that there are an infinity of times, but that time passes in discrete moments, and define Mp as 'Either it is at this moment the case that p or it will be the case at the next moment that p'. Again using infinite sequences of 1's and 3's for our 'values', the sequence for Mp now has a 1 wherever p has a 1 either at that place or at the place immediately after it, otherwise a 3. For example, if the sequence for p goes thus:

$$13113333311313331, \text{ etc.},$$

the sequence for Mp will go thus:

$$11113333111113311, \text{ etc.}$$

The conditions for Lp are obtained by replacing '1' by '3' and '3' by '1' in our description of the conditions for Mp, and the sequence with 1's only is still the designated value. This matrix verifies all formulae in the system which Feys calls T (shown by Sobociński[1] to be equivalent to von Wright's system M), in which the propositional calculus is supplemented by the definition of M as NLN, the rule to infer $L\alpha$ from α, and the axioms $CLpp$ and $CLCpqCLpLq$; but it does not verify either S4 formulae like $CLpLLp$ and $CMMpMp$ or S5 formulae like $CMpLMp$ and $CMLpLp$, and it can be shown that there is an infinity of modalities in this system, i.e. that MMp can have a different value from Mp, $MMMp$ different from both MMp and Mp, and so on.[2] Thus with the above example we have

$$p = 13113333311313331, \text{ etc.}$$
$$Mp = 11113333111113311, \text{ etc.}$$
$$MMp = 11113331111113111, \text{ etc.}$$
$$MMMp = 11113311111111111, \text{ etc.}$$

The failure of $CMMpMp$ could be illustrated by a case in which p is not true at the time of utterance, nor at the moment immediately succeeding it (so that Mp, 'p either now or at the next moment' is false), but is true at the moment after that (so that 'It will be the case at the next moment that it will be the case at the next moment that p' is true, and along with it MMp, i.e. 'It either is or will immediately be the case that it either is or will immediately be the case that p').

These parts of tense-logic, then, are modal logics in the sense of Łukasiewicz, and are capable of being represented as many-valued truth-functional logics. There is one ground, however, on

---

[1] B. Sobociński, 'On a Modal System of Feys–von Wright', *Journal of Computing Systems*, vol. i, No. 3 (July 1953).

[2] I have in fact obtained my matrix by suitably modifying one used by J. C. C. McKinsey in his 'Proof that there are infinitely many modalities in Lewis's system S2', *JSL*, v (1940), pp. 110–12, and by Sobociński, op. cit., to prove the same for T.

which their genuinely modal character might be queried; for
there are logicians who deny that 'statements' which may have
different truth-values at different times are really complete or
'closed' statements. This seems to be Professor Quine's view,[1]
and it has received substantial though discriminating support
from Professor Smart.[2] So far as I can understand it, this view
works out more or less as follows: The statement 'It was true last
May that I was eating chocolates'—or as I would put it in my
more mechanical language 'It was the case last May that I am
eating chocolates', with the 'am' signifying the presentness of
my eating at that past time—really means something like 'It is
(timelessly) true of May 1955 that it is (timelessly) a time at
which I am (timelessly) eating chocolates'. No doubt this needs
some further tidying up, but the important point, and the one
on which I am sure I do not misrepresent the exponents of this
view, is that what appears to assert that something *was the case at*
a certain time is treated as really asserting that something—
something grammatically a little different, of course—*is timelessly true of* that time. And of course if the second something
really *is* timelessly true of the time in question, then the statement that it is, is timelessly plain true. Instead of statements
being true and false *at* different times, we have predicates being
timelessly true and false *of* different times. So that in the form
Utp, '*p* at *t*', *p* does not really stand for a statement, and *Ut* does
not really stand for a statement-forming operator on statements; rather, *t* stands for a time, and *p* for a predicate timelessly attached to that time, and it is not until the two are put
together that we have a statement at all. The *U* is pointless, and
the whole would be less misleadingly written as *pt*, or better
still *φt*. Similarly in the form *ΣtUtp*, 'For some *t*, *p* at *t*', *p* does
not stand for a statement but for a timeless predicate of times,
and only the expression as a whole stands for a statement, and
would be better written as *Σtpt* or *Σtφt*. If, then, we introduce
the form *Mp* as an abbreviation for *ΣtUtp*, or better for *Σtφt*, *M*
is an operator which forms statements out of predicates, and so
is not a modal operator at all, at least in what appears to be
Łukasiewicz's stricter sense.

   This is not an objection which I would expect to come from

[1] W. V. Quine, 'Mr. Strawson on Logical Theory', *Mind* (1953), § 4, pp. 440–3.
[2] J. J. C. Smart, 'Spatialising Time', *Mind* (1955), pp. 239–41.

Łukasiewicz himself, since his own 3-valued logic of 1920 seems to have been originally designed to formalize a theory of Aristotle's about the truth-values of statements with their tenses taken seriously. Still, the objection should be met, wherever it originates. But what is it to 'meet' an objection of this sort? Where deep-rooted prejudices are in conflict there are no knock-down arguments, but at least the consequences of the various positions can be drawn. It is not yet easy to see what these consequences are; but we may see them more clearly if we consider what is at first sight an objection of quite a different sort to the tense-logical systems which have been sketched so far.

My own misgivings about these systems began from a consideration of what I call the Barcan formula, because it was laid down as an axiom by Mrs. Ruth Barcan Marcus in one of the first attempts to combine the Lewis modal systems with quantification theory.[1] In the Łukasiewicz symbolism this formula would be

$$CM\Sigma x\phi x\Sigma xM\phi x,$$

and we might read it as 'If it is possible that something ϕ's then there is something which possibly ϕ's'. If we took Mp to mean 'It either is or has been or will be the case that p' (and that is what our $\Sigma tUtp$ boils down to), then the formula would assert that if it either is or has been or will be the case that something ϕ's, then there is something which either ϕ's or has ϕ'd or will ϕ. For example, if it either is or has been or will be the case that someone is flying to the moon, then there is someone who either is flying or has flown or will fly to the moon. And it is not easy to be quite happy about this. For suppose that in fact someone will fly to the moon some day, but not anyone who now exists. Then it will be true that it either is, has been, or will be the case that someone is flying to the moon; but it will not be true that there is someone who either is flying or has flown or will fly to the moon.

If, however, we drop the Barcan formula on grounds such as this, that will not be the end of the matter. It is true that in Mrs. Barcan Marcus's original system it was simply a special axiom adjoined to quantification theory plus one of the weaker Lewis

[1] Ruth C. Barcan, 'A Functional Calculus of First Order based on Strict Implication', *Journal of Symbolic Logic*, vol. xi (1946), p. 2, Prop. 11.

systems; but I have shown elsewhere[1] that if we combine quantification theory with the Lewis system S5 we are no longer free
to adjoin the Barcan formula or not as we please, for from this
combination it is provable as a theorem. So if we are determined
to drop the Barcan formula in its tense-logical interpretation,
we must either deny that ordinary quantification theory holds
in this field, or deny that a set of postulates equivalent to those
for S5 can be a satisfactory set for the tense-logical L and M.
And if something must go from these postulates for L and M,
then something must go also from the special postulates for the
operator Ut from which we derived the S5 ones for L and M;
and the objection will in the end reach even farther back too,
namely into any postulates for the more fundamental Fn-Pn calculus from which the offending ones for Ut may be deducible.
The dubiety of the Barcan formula is thus transmissible to the
entire structure of the tense-logic we have so far erected.

If, on the other hand, we can accept the basic assumptions of
what we may call the Quine–Smart way of handling time
distinctions, we are not subjected to these tensions. Not that in
this tenseless logic we can do away with the equivalent of the
Barcan formula—on the contrary. For when its tense-logical
interpretation is written out in full the formula becomes:

$$C\Sigma t Ut\Sigma x \phi x \Sigma x \Sigma t Ut \phi x,$$

and when the form $Ut\phi x$ is replaced by the simple ϕxt, this in
turn becomes

$$C\Sigma t \Sigma x \phi xt \Sigma x \Sigma t \phi xt$$

or more briefly $C\Sigma tx\phi xt\Sigma xt\phi xt,$

which is an elementary formula of quantification theory. Intuitively, there can be no getting away from it—if there is a
time of which it is timelessly true that something ϕ's at it, then
quite unquestionably there is an object of which it is timelessly
true that it ϕ's at some time. Or to put it another way, if there
is somewhere a timeless instantiation of the dyadic relation-
form ϕxt, then there is not only a time t but an object x timelessly standing as a term in that relation. How could it be
otherwise?—neither a time nor anything else can just 'stand in a

[1] A. N. Prior, 'Modality and Quantification in S5', *Journal of Symbolic Logic*,
March 1956.

relation' without there being anything that it stands in that relation *to*. But on this view of the matter, neither the antecedent nor the consequent of the Barcan formula says anything at all about the *present* existence of the *x* which ϕ's at *t*. That is, neither $\Sigma t x \phi x t$ nor $\Sigma x t \phi x t$ says anything at all about the boundaries in the time-dimension of the smudge on space-time which does duty for the object *x* in this logic (except of course that the time *t* lies within those boundaries).

This, then, is one way of relieving the tension I have described. But it is not the only way. Another way would be to take up the task of reviewing and revising our original set of postulates for tense-logic; and if that is done, we may be in a better position to compare tense-logic and tenseless logic and to make our choice between them.

IV

A Re-examination of our Tense-logical Postulates

JUST what is wrong with the Barcan formula $CM\Sigma x\phi x\Sigma xM\phi x$ when it is taken to mean

'If it is, has been, or will be the case that something ϕ's, then there is something which is ϕ-ing, has ϕ'd or will ϕ'?

The counter-example we have given to it would also do to refute the more elementary formula $CF\Sigma x\phi x\Sigma xF\phi x$,

'If it will be the case that something ϕ's, then there is something which will ϕ';

and we will find it simpler to concentrate at first on this form, which entails the other. The trouble with it is clearly that the consequent asserts that something already existing will ϕ, while the antecedent does not commit us to that much. So the only ground one can think of for assenting to it would be a conviction that whatever is going to exist at some future time exists already. And if $CF\Sigma x\phi x\Sigma xF\phi x$ is laid down as expressing a logical law, i.e. as yielding with all concrete substitutions for its variables a statement which is true whenever it is made, it can only be justified by the assumption that whatever exists at any time exists at all times, i.e. the assumption that all real individuals are sempiternal.

It may be that this assumption is capable of metaphysical justification. With regard to our counter-example—that perhaps there will be someone flying to the moon although it will not be anyone now existing—it may be argued that persons are not individuals in the sense in which the x's and y's of quantification theory stand for names of individuals, and that all *genuine* individuals do exist at all times. On this view, the point about the flight to the moon is that although the collection of genuine individuals which will perform the flight has not yet come to constitute a person, these genuine individuals—electrons or whatever they might be—do exist now, and always have done and always will. And this would save the Barcan formula, for the difference appealed to now turns out to be not one between $F\Sigma x\phi x$ and $\Sigma xF\phi x$, and so between $M\Sigma x\phi x$ and $\Sigma xM\phi x$, but one between forms more like $F\Sigma xK\psi x\phi x$ and $\Sigma xK\psi xF\phi x$, 'It will be the case that something is a person and flies' and 'Something is a person of whom it will be the case that he flies'.

But I doubt whether this story about sempiternal electrons is good physics, and am sure it is not good logic. That is to say, even if it be true that whatever exists at any time exists at all times, there is surely no *inconsistency* in denying it, and a *logic* of time-distinctions ought to be able to proceed without assuming it. It must be admitted, however, that when this assumption is driven out the front door it is liable to return through the back. In discussing our counter-example to the Barcan formula we might, for example, say that the flight to the moon may be accomplished by 'someone who does not exist yet but will exist later on'. And this way of talking seems to imply that *there is* an x such that x does not exist yet but will exist later on. But what sort of an x could this be? An object, apparently, which does not yet exist but nevertheless can already be talked about, or at all events can be a value for the variables bound by our quantifiers. And if this object, although it does not yet exist, can already be talked about, or can be a value for our bound variables, presumably it is in this position at all times—it is at all times an object, even if it is not at all times an existent object. And of course if the bound variables in the Barcan formula are supposed to range over all objects in this wide sense of 'object'— all the items in this supposed permanent pool of things that are, have been, or will be—it can again be justified. If it will be the case that one of these objects, whether an existent one or one still waiting for existence, flies to the moon, then *there is* one of these objects, either an existent one or one of the others, which will fly to the moon.

This idea of a permanent pool of objects, some now existing and some only having existed or going to exist, seems to be presupposed in the medieval theory of *ampliatio*, according to which what things a general term can stand for depends in part on the tense or mood of the verb with which it is used.[1] In 'Some man is running', the word 'man' can stand for any man now

[1] Cf. E. A. Moody, op. cit.

existing; but in 'Some man will be running' it can stand also for a man who merely will exist, and in 'Some man could be running' it can stand for a man who merely could exist—in the one case, *supponit pro futuris*, and in the other *pro possibilibus*, and not only *pro praesentibus*. The metaphysics involved in this way of talking is apt to strike the modern reader as weird—

> And what rough beast, its hour come round at last,
> Is slouching towards Bethlehem to be born?

But let us not exaggerate this queerness. What this comprehensive objecthood amounts to is simply that *there are already facts about these objects*, even if they are not yet existent. Even a tough-minded disciple of Quine and Smart might defend this way of talking, on the ground that it is only a way of expressing, in the inadequate locutions of ordinary speech, the fact that although an object may only *occupy* a finite region of space-time, it stands timelessly in a variety of relations to *all* space-time regions.

All the same, it should be possible in tense-logic to do without even this attenuated form of the sempiternity hypothesis. My own objections to it would run somewhat as follows: Where x stands for a proper name, it seems to me that the form 'x exists' must be logically equivalent to, and definable as, 'There are facts about x', $\Sigma \phi \phi x$. If there *are* facts about x, I cannot see what *further* fact about x would consist in its existing. And when x no longer exists or does not yet exist, but there are nevertheless facts about x now, I do not know what the present-tense facts about x would be. Is this dead or unborn man now blue-eyed, for example? If we say that, whatever he was or will be, he is not blue-eyed now because he does not exist now, this suggests that all present-tense *denials* are true of this x. But then it would be as true to deny that he is *not* blue-eyed as it would to deny that he *is* blue-eyed, and I do not think this is quite what a supporter of this theory would intend. So while it is clear that on this view some facts about x would entail x's present existence and some would not, it is not at all clear which facts would go into which box. In the tenseless language of Quine and Smart, I suppose the corresponding problem would be to differentiate between *occupying* a space-time region and standing in some other relation to a space-time region, and for all I know the problem in this form may be a comparatively simple one, but it does not strike me as being a *logical* problem. Point one, then, is that we want a tense-logic in which we can equate '*x* exists' with 'There are facts about *x*'.

Secondly, if we do not admit this conception of a permanent pool of existent and non-existent objects, we must think differently of the range of values for bound variables in this logic. 'There *is* an *x* which ϕ's' must be understood as true if we can now frame a true statement of the form '*x* ϕ's'; and 'There *will be* an *x* tomorrow which ϕ's', or 'It will be the case tomorrow that there is an *x* which ϕ's', must be understood as true if we will be able tomorrow to form a true statement of the form '*x* ϕ's', even if it be a statement which not only would not be true now but could not be framed now. In other words, in the form 'There will be an *x* tomorrow which ϕ's', the bound variable *x* has as yet no range of values at all, and its truth-value depends, so far as it depends on a range of values, on the range of values which the bound variable in 'There *is* an *x* which ϕ's' will acquire tomorrow. And what it now states is not a fact *about* any of tomorrow's objects, though if the statement is true there will be an *x* tomorrow with a fact about it of the form '*x* ϕ's'.

This will have to do as a preliminary sketch of the kind of position I am trying to formalize. All that I have said so far about its formalization is that we need a system in which the Barcan formula is not provable, and that the Barcan formula is provable if we adjoin the ordinary theory of quantification to a tense-logic with the structure of Lewis's S5, so that that combination is definitely not the system we are after. Before considering what we must drop from S5 and what we can retain, it will be as well to look into the possibility that it is the quantification theory that needs to be altered when tensed propositions are admitted. One argument that has been put to me[1] in favour of this view is the following: One of the elementary laws of ordinary quantification theory is the law that if *y* ϕ's then there is something that ϕ's, $C\phi y\Sigma x\phi x$. But there are untrue propositions of this form; for instance, the proposition 'If Alexander rode Bucephalus, then there exists an object which Alexander rode', or in our schematized language, 'If it has been the case that Bucephalus is ridden by Alexander, there exists an object

---

[1] By Professor W. T. Parry, acting as a referee for the *Journal of Symbolic Logic*.

of which it has been the case that it is ridden by Alexander'. Here the antecedent is now true, and the consequent now false, anything ridden by Alexander having long ceased to exist.

This objection can be met by saying that since Alexander's horse has ceased to exist the word 'Bucephalus' can no longer count as a logical proper name—that is, it cannot in principle be replaced by a demonstrative—and so is not substitutable for y in the formula $C\phi y\Sigma x\phi x$. On this view all statements which are ostensibly about Bucephalus are in fact not singular but quantified statements involving what we may describe, in the manner of Quine, as the property of 'Bucephalizing'. The same is true, of course, of statements ostensibly about Alexander, since he has ceased to exist too; but as he does not affect our argument we can leave him alone. Our apparent counter-example now becomes a piece of shorthand for

> 'If it has been the case that something is the only Bucephalizer and is ridden by Alexander, then there is something of which it has been the case that it is ridden by Alexander'.

This is not of the form $CP\phi y\Sigma xP\phi x$, which would be a special case of the form $C\phi y\Sigma x\phi x$, and obtainable from it by the substitution $\phi/P\phi$; it is rather of the form $CP\Sigma xK\psi x\phi x\Sigma xP\phi x$, which is not a special case of the form $C\phi y\Sigma x\phi x$ at all, and is not obtainable from it by any substitution. And it is fairly clear that if only what is properly nameable may be referred to by an unbound y and only what now exists is properly nameable, then any assertion of the form $C\phi y\Sigma x\phi x$—which can now be read as 'If *this* ϕ's, then there is something that ϕ's'—will be true, even if it is of the sub-form $CP\phi y\Sigma xP\phi x$, 'If it has been the case that *this* ϕ's, there is something of which it has been the case that it ϕ's'.

I am a little uncomfortable about this view that we cannot properly name objects which have ceased to exist, like Bucephalus; but I do not see any way of avoiding it—if we say that we *can* properly name them, and that there *are* facts directly about them, we are exposed to all the difficulties which were earlier shown to arise with the general theory that there are non-existent objects. Instinctively, all the same, we are happier about granting that we cannot properly name, and that there are no facts directly about, objects which *do not yet* exist; in particular, there are some very powerful arguments to this effect in Professor Ryle's Tarner Lectures.[1] So without giving way on the wider issue, I shall as far as possible draw my examples in what follows from this less disputable area.

Returning to the problem of eliminating the Barcan formula from tense-logic, it is clear that if we are not going to tamper with quantification theory we must re-examine the S5-like postulates for tense-logic itself. And when we do so, it becomes apparent quickly enough that we could not save all these postulates even if we did tamper with quantification theory, for some of them will not do even when their propositional variables are taken to stand for unquantified forms.

Let us begin with the essential point. If I use the word 'I' as a logical proper name, then if I say 'I do not exist', meaning 'There are no facts about me', this is self-contradictory. For if it were true that there are no facts about me, then there would be *this* fact about me, that there are no facts about me, and so it would be false. Nor, of course, could this statement be other than self-contradictory at any time at which it is possible to make it. The forms $PnN\Sigma\phi\phi x$, 'It was the case n days ago that x does not exist', and $FnN\Sigma\phi\phi x$, 'It will be the case n days hence that x does not exist', can therefore only stand for false propositions. On the other hand, a statement of the form $NPn\Sigma\phi\phi x$, 'It was not the case n days ago that x exists', may very well be true, on the assumption that there are non-sempiternal individuals. For example, it was not the case 100 years ago that I existed; there were, I would contend, no facts about me then—not even this fact of there being no facts about me at that time; though it is *now* a fact that there were no facts about me then. What we cannot say is that it *was* the case 100 years ago that I did *not* exist. So we must distinguish between the form 'It was not the case that p' and 'It was the case that not p'. We must likewise and in consequence distinguish between the forms 'It is not true at all times that p', NLp, and 'It is true at some time that not p', MNp; for example, 'It is not true at all times that there are facts about me', and 'It is true at some time that there are no facts about me'. And of course we must distinguish between 'It is not true at all times that not p', $NLNp$, and 'It is true at some time that p', or Mp. For example, it is not true at all times that I am not a logician without being a logician, for before I

[1] G. Ryle, *Dilemmas*, pp. 26–27. Cf. also Peirce, *Collected Papers*, 4. 172.

existed there was not even this fact about me; but this does not mean that there is any time at which I *am* a logician without being a logician. And into this last case, it may be noted, quantification does not enter, except so far as M and L contain quantifications.

A word should be said about this last point. There may seem to be an inconsistency with quantification theory in denying the equivalence of M and NLN; for in quantification theory 'Something ϕ's' is equivalent to 'Not everything doesn't ϕ', so how can we preserve quantification theory and deny that 'At some time p' is equivalent to 'Not at all times not p'? What makes this possible is that although, as defined in our Ut system, M and NLN *contain* quantifiers, it is not true that they simply *are* quantifiers. For the operator M is not equated with the quantifier Σt, 'For some t', but rather with the operator ΣtUt, 'For some t, at t', and L is similarly not just Πt but ΠtUt. So we have not two but three forms to relate, namely

(1) $\Sigma tUtp$, 'For some t, p at t'.

(2) $N\Pi tNUtp$, 'Not for all t, not p-at-t'.

(3) $N\Pi tUtNp$, 'Not for all t, not-p at t'.

Of these, (2) is equivalent to (1) by quantification theory; and it is a reasonable equivalence even with our present type of subject-matter. If not all times are times such that it is not then the case that p, then some time is a time such that it *is* then the case that p. But it is not (2) but (3) which abbreviates to $NLNp$, and (3) is not equivalent by quantification theory either to (2) or to (1). What (2) says is that not all times are *times such that it is not then the case that p*; what (3) says, on the other hand, is that not all times are *times such that it is then the case that not p*; and in our original proof of the equivalence of $NLNp$ and Mp, we did not pass from (3) to (2) by quantification theory, but by the axiom $CNUtpUtNp$, 'If it is not the case at t that p, then it is the case at t that not p'. This is clearly a formula that must be dropped from a tense-logic with proper names for non-sempiternal objects; for example, from the fact that it was not the case in 1850 that there were then facts about me, it does not follow that it *was* the case in 1850 that there were *not* then facts about me.

I should like to emphasize that what I am proposing at this point is not an abandonment of the law of excluded middle. We still have 'Either p or not p' as a law, and therefore we still have 'Either it was the case at t that p or it was not the case at t that p', $AUtpNUtp$; what must go is not this but 'Either it was the case that p or it was the case that not p', $AUtpUtNp$, but this is not a substitution in $ApNp$, so the law of excluded middle does not require us to affirm it.

The rejection of the Barcan formula involves a similar distinction between $Ut\Sigma x\phi x$, 'At t there is something which ϕ's', and $\Sigma xUt\phi x$, 'There is something which ϕ's-at-t'. The consequent of the Barcan formula, tense-logically interpreted, amounts to $\Sigma x\Sigma tUt\phi x$, 'There is an x such that, for some t, x ϕ's at t', and the form $\Sigma t\Sigma xUt\phi x$, 'For some t, there is something which ϕ's-at-t', is equivalent to this by quantification theory. But the antecedent of the Barcan formula is not this last but $\Sigma tUt\Sigma x\phi x$, 'For some t, at t there is something which ϕ's', and this is not equivalent to the other.

In a logic of the Quine–Smart type, as we have already noted, this distinction cannot be made; nor, in such a logic, can we make the more fundamental distinction between $NUtp$ and $UtNp$. In this logic, to say that it was not the case in 1850 that p, is just to say that a certain property is timelessly absent from the date 1850; and to say that it was the case in 1850 that not p, is to say that the contradictory of that property, that is, the absence of it, timelessly characterizes this date; these two cannot be anything but equivalent, and to assert one and deny the other is just to contradict oneself. Some will feel, I think, that it *is* self-contradictory to say that it was not the case in 1850 that there were then any facts about me, *and* that it was not the case in 1850 that there were no facts about me; and whoever does feel that this is self-contradictory will welcome a system which makes the contradiction obvious. Others will feel that the combination I have stated is not self-contradictory, and that any system in which we cannot make the distinctions necessary to reconcile its two parts is to that extent defective, even if it is a handy system to use for various special purposes. We have here, perhaps, something like a plain issue; and having stated it, I shall say no more for the time being about the Quine–Smart system.

Of the Gödelian postulates for S5, then, we must in tense-logic drop the definition of *M* as *NLN*. *Mp* or 'Sometimes *p*' does imply 'Not always not *p*', *NLNp*, but the converse does not hold —'Not always not *p*' does not imply 'Sometimes *p*'. Nor can we keep the rule that if α expresses a law so does *L*α. For example, the form *Cpp* expresses a law; any statement of this form, such as 'If I am a logician I am a logician', is true whenever it can be made. But *LCpp* does not express a law, for some statements of this form are not true. 'It is, always has been, and always will be the case that if I am a logician I am a logician' is not true; for it was not the case in 1850 that if I am a logician I am a logician—there were no facts at all about me then. On the other hand, we do have the rule that if α expresses a law so does *NMN*α. Even if a concrete statement which is logically true is not for that reason true always, because it is not always statable, we can still say that it is never false. This difference brings out the fact that *NMNp* is a weaker form than *Lp*, just as *NLNp* is a weaker form than *Mp*.

Of the axioms, there seems nothing wrong with *CLpp* and *CLCpqCLpLq*, but *CNLpLNLp*, 'If it is not always the case that *p* then it is always not always the case that *p*', will not do. It is not always the case that I am smoking, but it has not always been the case that this is not always the case—in 1850, for example, it was not the case that it is not always the case that I am smoking. On the other hand, some of the characteristic 'reduction theorems' of S5, not provable in any of the weaker Lewis systems, do hold in this revised tense-logic; for example *CMLpLp*, which in ordinary modal logic asserts that whatever could be necessary is actually necessary, and in tense-logic asserts that if it is sometimes the case that *p* is always the case, then *p* is always-the-case now. If *p* were ever unstatable, it could not at any time be the case that *p* is always the case; so if it *is* sometimes the case that *p* is always the case, *p* must be always statable, and it must be always true too.

In sum, our postulates must be weakened, but the weakening required is at some rather odd places, and is not such as to leave us with one of the weaker Lewis systems. For *CMLpLp* does not hold in any Lewis system weaker than S5; on the other hand, in all the Lewis systems *M* is equivalent to *NLN* and *L* to *NMN*. These equivalences also hold in the Ł-modal system; so that is not what we want either (apart from other objections to that system, e.g. that $CMLpLp$ does *not* hold in it), though the Ł-modal system does have the merit, from our present point of view, of not containing the rule to infer $L\alpha$ from α. Of modal systems hitherto developed, the only one of importance that does not contain the equivalence of M and NLN or L and NMN is that which would be obtained by subjoining postulates which would normally yield S_5—for example, my own rules L1, L2, M1, and M2[1]—to Heyting's intuitionist calculus instead of to the classical propositional calculus. In this modal system, as in the tense-logic towards which we are now feeling our way, we have the laws $CMpNLNp$ and $CLpNMNp$ but not their converses; for M1, etc., only yield these by the help of the law $CNNpp$, which does not hold in Heyting's calculus. But even this system will not quite suit our purposes; for on the one hand we have found no reason for tampering with the classical propositional calculus; and on the other hand, even when their propositional-calculus basis is thus reduced, the ordinary rules will yield on the modal side *more* than we really want. For example, although they will not yield $CNMNpLp$, they will yield $CNMpLNp$, as follows:

1. Cpp
2. $CCpqCNqNp$
   $$1 \times M2 = 3.$$
3. $CpMp$
   $$2q/Mp = C3—4.$$
4. $CNMpNp$
   $$4 \times L2 = 5.$$
5. $CNMpLNp$

[1] As in my *Formal Logic*, pp. 202 and 306–7 (postulate set 6.5), but with L2 and M1 amended to

L2: $C\alpha\beta \rightarrow C\alpha L\beta$, provided that all propositional variables in α are modalized.
M1: $C\alpha\beta \rightarrow CM\alpha\beta$, provided that all propositional variables in β are modalized.

(Łukasiewicz has shown that with the weaker provisos on L2 and M1 given in *Formal Logic*, $CpLp$ and $CMpp$ would be deducible.) These rules (thus amended) are the modal counterparts of Łukasiewicz's rules for quantifiers, and the above-mentioned calculus is the modal counterpart of the intuitionist theory of quantification developed in Heyting's 'On Weakened Quantification', *Journal of Symbolic Logic*, vol. xi (1946), pp. 119–21.

(only the lack of *CNNpp* prevents us from passing from this, with the substitution *p/Np*, to *CNMNpLp*).[1]

We want, then, a system which (*a*) as far as its M-L structure is concerned, is contained in the Lewis system S5 but does not contain it, and which contains but is not contained in the classical propositional calculus, but which (*b*) neither contains nor is contained in the weaker Lewis systems S1–S4, or the modalized intuitionist calculus, or the Ł-model system, though the first two of these are also contained in S5 and the first and the last also contain the classical propositional calculus. Calling our desideratum the system Q, its relation (as an M-L system) to these others, and their own interrelations, may be set out diagrammatically as follows (using an arrow for containing, CPC for the classical propositional calculus, IPC for Heyting's, and MIPC for its modalized extension):

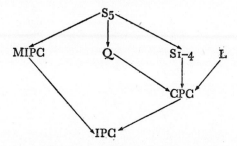

But with all its differences from the others, our revised system will meet the first six of Łukesiewicz's conditions for being a modal system, since we have no reason for denying *CLpp*, 'What is true always is true now', or *CpMp*, 'What is true now is true

---

[1] Between forms which are equivalent in the Lewis calculi, the following relations hold when the classical propositional calculus is replaced by Heyting's:

    (i) *Lp→NNLp→(LNNp, NNLNNp, NMNp)*.
    (ii) *Mp→MNNp→(NNMp, NNMNNp, NLNp)*.
    (iii) *MNp→(NNMNp, NLNNp)→NLp*.
    (iv) *(LNp, NNLNp, NMNNp, NMp)*.

Bracketed forms are equivalent, and the arrow indicates one-sided implication. In our revised tense-logical system what we want is rather

    (i) *(Lp, NNLp, LNNp, NNLNNp)→NMNp*.
    (ii) *(Mp, MNNp, NNMp, NNMNNp)→NLNp*.
    (iii) *(MNp, NNMNp)→(NLNNp, NLp)*.
    (iv) *(LNp, NNLNp)→(NMNNp, NMp)*.

at some time', or for affirming as laws either *CpLp*, *CMpp*, *Mp*, or *NLp*. And it is possible to represent it as a many-valued system—this will, in fact, be the most precise mathematical representation of it that is possible until a complete set of postulates for it is found.

V

The System Q

WITH a view to producing a many-valued representation of the revised tense-logic sketched rather negatively in our last, let us again begin by supposing that there are only two times, but let us suppose them to be not today and tomorrow but, for a change, today and yesterday. And we shall assume that today is the day on which we are using this system, so that its variables can stand for any statement which we can make today, whether we could have made it yesterday or not. The possibility that some of our statements could not have been made yesterday enlarges the possible values of our statements from four to six: (1) true at both times; (2) true today and unstatable yesterday; (3) true today and false yesterday; (4) false today but true yesterday; (5) false today and unstatable yesterday; and (6) false at both times. And if p is a statement which could not have been made yesterday, then any compound statement containing it, such as Np or Kpq or Mp or Lp, could not have been made yesterday either. Mp we take to mean 'p at some time', and Lp to mean 'p both times'. The values 1 and 2 are both designated, since a formula expresses a logical law if its concrete substitutions are true whenever they are statable, i.e. either true at both times or true today and unstatable yesterday.

With these guiding principles, it is easy to construct tables for K, N, M, and L, and work out others for C, A, E, etc. The tables for N, M, L and NMN work out as follows:

p	Np	Mp	Lp	$NMNp$
*1	6	1	1	1
*2	5	2	5	2
3	4	1	6	6
4	3	1	6	6
5	2	5	5	5
6	1	6	6	6

The difference between the tables for L and NMN should be noted. It occurs where p has the value 2, i.e. true today but unstatable yesterday. In this case p is not true both times, and today we can say that it is not, i.e. can deny Lp, but yesterday it was unstatable, so that Lp has the value 5, false today and unstatable yesterday. But in this same case, with p true today and unstatable yesterday, not-p is false today and unstatable yesterday; so that not-p is not true at either time, and this fact—that not-p is not true at either time—is true today but was unstatable yesterday, i.e. $NMNp$ has the value 2. From this difference others follow. If α expresses a law, i.e. always has one of the values 1 and 2, then $NMN\alpha$ always has one of these values, i.e. expresses a law too. But the same is not true of $L\alpha$. $L\alpha$ in fact never takes the value 2 at all, and could only have the value 1 for all values of its variables if α itself had the value 1 for all values of its variables. This in turn could only be so if the variables in α were not capable of taking either of the values 2 and 5; for any formula of which any part takes one of these values must itself take one of them. This follows from the fact that any function of what was unstatable yesterday will itself have been unstatable yesterday. But ordinary propositional variables are not restricted in their possible values to those other than 2 and 5. Hence in the system Q, considered as a system in N, K, L, and M with ordinary propositional variables only, there can be no laws of the form $L\alpha$ at all. In this it is like the Ł-modal system; but it is unlike it in that in the Ł-modal system there are not only no laws of the form $L\alpha$ but no individual true propositions of the form Lp (the values of such propositions being confined, in that system, to 2, 3, and 4). In the system Q, on the other hand, Lp does have the value 1 when p has it, and there are statements for which p can stand which do have this value, though there are no forms which have it for all values, including 2 and 5, of their constituent variables.

The tables for K, C, and A in this system are as follows:

K	1	2	3	4	5	6
*1	1	2	3	4	5	6
*2	2	2	2	5	5	5
3	3	2	3	6	5	6
4	4	5	6	4	5	6
5	5	5	5	5	5	5
6	6	5	6	6	5	6

C	1	2	3	4	5	6
*1	1	2	3	4	5	6
*2	2	2	2	5	5	5
3	1	2	1	4	5	4
4	1	2	3	1	2	3
5	2	2	2	2	2	2
6	1	2	1	1	2	1

A	1	2	3	4	5	6
*1	1	2	1	1	2	1
*2	2	2	2	2	2	2
3	1	2	3	1	2	3
4	1	2	1	4	5	4
5	2	2	2	5	5	5
6	1	2	3	4	5	6

$CNMN pLp$ will be found to take the value 5, which is not designated, when $p = 2$, and $CNLN pMp$ takes the same value when $p = 5$. These results correspond to our intuitive objections to the S5 type of tense-logic. If p is something like 'I am both a logican and not a logician', which is false whenever it is statable but is not always statable, Np is not statable when p is not, and so is not always true, so that 'Not always not p', $NLNp$, is true when statable, i.e. has the value 2; while since p is never true, Mp or 'Sometimes p' is false when it is statable, i.e. has the value 5; and $C25 = 5$. $CNLpLNLp$ has the undesignated value 5 when $p = 2$ or 5. The other two Gödelian axioms, and the classical propositional calculus, are verified; but besides being more tedious to work out, this result is of less significance, for although whatever is falsified by these tables will be something we do not want in Q, we will not want all that they verify, since some formulae which they verify merely reflect the fiction that there are only two times.

These 6-valued tables are in fact just the first step towards the matrix with an infinite number of elements which would give us the exact many-valued equivalent of the system Q.

We may describe this matrix as follows:

(1) Each of its elements may be associated with an infinite sequence of numbers, which must be 1, 2, or 3, and of which the first must be 1 or 3. Intuitively we can think of these numbers as indicating whether the proposition is true, unstatable, or false at each one of an infinity of times, the first place in the sequence representing the present time.

(2) The sequence for Np is determined by the sequence for p as follows:

$$N(xyz...) = (Nx)(Ny)(Nz)...,$$

where the table for N considered as operating on a single number is

x	Nx
1	3
2	2
3	1

(3) The sequence for Kpq is determined by the sequences for p and for q as follows:

$$K(xyz...)(x'y'z'...) = (Kxx')(Kyy')(Kzz')...,$$

where the table for K considered as operating on a pair of single numbers is

K	1	2	3
1	1	2	3
2	2	2	2
3	3	2	3

(4) The sequence for Lp is determined by the sequence for p as follows:

   (a) If the sequence for p is that consisting of 1's only the sequence for Lp is the same.

   (b) If the sequence for p contains any 2's, then in the sequence for Lp these 2's keep their place unaltered, and all other places are occupied by 3's.

   (c) If the sequence for p contains no 2's, but contains 3's, whether it also contains 1's or not, the sequence for Lp is that consisting of 3's only.

(5) The sequence for Mp is determined by the sequence for p as follows:

   (a) Where the sequence for p consists either of 3's only or of 3's and 2's only, the sequence for Mp is the same as the sequence for p.

   (b) Where the sequence for p contains 2's and 1's, whether it contains 3's or not, in the sequence for Mp the 2's keep their place unaltered and all other places are occupied by 1's.

   (c) Where the sequence for p contains no 2's, but does contain 1's, whether it contains 3's or not, the sequence for Mp is that consisting of 1's only.

(6) The designated sequences are all those which contain no 3's.

The way in which these rather complicated stipulations preserve the characteristic features of the 6-valued system, apart from those which reflect its underlying fiction of a limited number of times, may be illustrated by the non-equivalence of Lp and $NMNp$. The difference arises in those cases in which the sequence for p contains only 1's and 2's. The sequence for Np will then, by the above rules, contain only 3's and 2's, so that that for MNp will also contain only 3's and 2's, and the one for the negation of this, $NMNp$, will contain only 1's and 2's. But if the sequence for p contains only 1's and 2's, the sequence for Lp contains only 3's and 2's, and so is different from that for $NMNp$. Again, if a formula α expresses a logical law, i.e. if no sequences for statements of the given form contain 3's, then no sequences for statements of the corresponding form $NMN\alpha$ will contain 3's, but some for the form $L\alpha$, namely those where the sequences for α contain 2's as well as 1's, will contain 3's, so that $L\alpha$ will not express a law.

Both with the infinite matrix just sketched, and with the 6-valued approximation to it, there is a certain awkwardness about the verification of the rule of detachment. The difficulty arises at the following point: If we look at the 6-valued table for C, we will see that $C23 = 2$. That is, it is possible for both p and Cpq to have the designated value 2 when q has the undesignated value 3. Or using our more precise numbering of the values, p and Cpq could both have the value (12) when q has the value (13). For example, 'I exist' and 'If I exist then someone other than God exists' could both be true today but (owing to my non-existence) unstatable yesterday, and therefore true whenever statable, even if 'Someone other than God exists' was yesterday definitely false. Similarly, with the infinite matrix, p and Cpq might both have designated sequences, containing no 3's, i.e. might both be true-whenever-statable, and q an undesignated sequence, provided that the q-sequence has a 3 only at places where the p-sequence has a 2, i.e. provided that q is only false at times when p is unstatable.

This fact does not mean that it is ever unsafe to pass from a specific proposition p and a specific Cpq to the corresponding q. For example, the inference of 'Someone other than God exists' from 'I exist' and 'If I exist then someone other than God exists' is a perfectly valid one; at any time when the premisses are true the conclusion is true also, and when the conclusion is *not* true the premisses are unstable and the inference not merely ought not to be but just cannot be made. It is, however, definitely unsafe to pass from the fact that a specific p (say 'I exist') and a specific Cpq (say 'If I exist then someone other than God exists') are both true whenever statable, to the conclusion that q ('Someone other than God exists') is true whenever statable.

What bearing has this upon the rule of detachment? The rule of detachment, it should be emphasized at the outset, is *not* the rule that from a specific p and Cpq we may infer q; nor is it the rule that from the truth-whenever-statable of a specific p and Cpq we may infer the truth-whenever-statable of q. The rule of detachment is the rule that if the formula α is so constructed that every proposition of this form has a designated value, and the formula $C\alpha\beta$ (where α is as before) also has this property, then β has this property. For example, the rule of detachment in Q would enable us to pass from the fact that anything of the form $CLpNMNp$ is true whenever statable, and that anything of the form $CCLpNMNpCMNpNLp$ (obtainable by substitution in $CCpNqCqNp$) is true whenever statable, to the conclusion that anything of the form $CMNpNLp$ is true whenever statable. If our value-tables are such that no two propositions p and Cpq both take a designated value unless q does, the rule of detachment will obviously hold, and with most systems this is how we show it will hold; but it also holds in some cases in which the value-tables are not of this sort, though the proof of it must then be more roundabout.

The position with regard to Q is as follows: Detachment can be shown to hold in Q itself, and it can also be shown to continue to hold when Q is enriched by name-variables, predicate variables, and quantifiers.[1] When, however, we enrich the

---

[1] The proof for Q is as follows: If there were a counter-example to detachment in Q it would be one in which every possible sequence for β which contained 3's would contain them only where the corresponding sequence for α contained 2's; the 'corresponding sequence for α' being that which results when all variables in α are assigned the same values as the same variables in β. Now a sequence for α can only contain a 2 where the sequence assigned to some variable in α has a 2; and if this variable occurred also in β, with the same value assigned to it, it would cause the sequence for β to have a 2 in that place also. Hence this variable—call it v—cannot occur in β. But in that case there will be no way of ensuring, by the very structure of β, that β will have 3's only where, and when, v has 2's, for the variables on the

symbolism of Q with name-*constants* also, detachment can only be retained with the proviso that β must not be inferred from α and $C\alpha\beta$ if α contains a name-constant which does not occur in β.[1] For example, if a is the name of a certain non-sempiternal object and b the name of a sempiternal object which once existed alone, the formula 'a is other than b' will have only one exemplification (itself), and this will be true whenever statable; the formula 'If a is other than b then something is other than b' will be in the same case; but the one exemplification of the formula 'Something is other than b' will be sometimes-false.

Among the rules and laws which are more obviously verified by our infinite matrix, it is worth listing the following:

R I: $\alpha \rightarrow NMN\alpha$.

R II: $C\alpha\beta \rightarrow CM\alpha M\beta$, provided that there is no variable in β which is not in α.

R III: $C\alpha\beta \rightarrow CL\alpha L\beta$, with the same proviso.

    (1) $CMpNLNp$.   (3) $CpMp$.

    (2) $CLpNMNp$.   (4) $CLCpqCLpLq$.

               (5) $CMLpLp$.

If we add to these as a further law the formula $CNLNpMp$, we can prove all of Gödel's postulates for S5, thus:

    (i) $CNLNpMp \rightarrow CNLNNpMNp$ (substitution, p/Np)

           $\rightarrow CNMNpLNNp$ (by $CCNpqCNqp$)

           $\rightarrow CNMNpLp$ (by $CNNpp$, R III, and syllogism).

Hence $\alpha \rightarrow L\alpha$ (by R I and the last result).

values of which the value of β does depend will be ones different from v and so varying independently of it. (This proof was hit upon independently by Dr. Alan Ross Anderson and myself.)

    When we introduce name-variables, so that there are other elementary propositional formulae (i.e. ones not containing other propositional formulae) beside propositional variables, the capacity for independent variation of different elementary propositional formulae may be restricted by their containing the same name-variables (for at any point at which a sequence for ϕx contains a 2, all simultaneously possible sequences for ψx will also contain a 2). However, the nature of the restriction makes it possible to extend the above proof to this extension of Q.

[1] The suggestion that this is the proviso required is due to my wife.

(ii) Since we have both $CMpNLNp$ and $CNLNpMp$, M and NLN are interchangeable in theses. The only doubt would be about modal contexts, but the proviso in R II and R III is automatically met when α and β only differ in one having M where the other has NLN.

(iii) $CpMp \rightarrow CNMpNp$ (by $CCpqCNqNp$)

   $\rightarrow CNMNpNNp$ (substitution, p/Np)

   $\rightarrow CNMNpp$ (by $CNNpp$)

   $\rightarrow CLpp$ (by (2)).

(iv) $CLCpqCLpLp$ is given as (4).

(v) $CMLpLp \rightarrow CNLNLpLp$ (by $CNLNpMp$)

   $\rightarrow CNLpLNLp$ (by $CCNpqCNqp$).

Since any postulate-set sufficient for the tense-logical system Q must yield R I–III and the laws (1)–(5), the addition of $CNLNpMp$ to any such postulate-set will, by the result just gained, give a system equivalent to S5. S5 may thus be thought of either as the result of adding $CMLpLp$ to a weaker Lewis system, say S2; or as the result of adding $CNNpp$ to the system formed by subjoining the rules M1, M2, L1, and L2 to Heyting's calculus; or as the result of adding $CNLNpMp$ to a postulate-set sufficient for the tense-logical system Q.

That, then, is the system Q. There is still very much more to be found out about it, but I shall not pursue its formal features further. What I want to say about it now is that it seems to me a useful calculus not only in the field of tense-logic but also in the field of modal logic as ordinarily understood. For if tense-logic is haunted by the myth that whatever exists at any time exists at all times, ordinary modal logic is haunted by the myth that whatever exists exists necessarily. If 'I exist' means 'There are facts about me', how should it be possible that I should not exist? If we so interpet 'It could be that p' that it *is* true if and only if p *could be* true, then my non-existence is something that could not be, since 'I do not exist', 'There are no facts about me', is not a thing that could be true. But in the ordinary systems 'It could not be that I do not exist' entails 'It is bound to be the case that I do exist', which makes gods of us all. Similarly, if it is necessary that if I am a logician I am a logician, it is necessary that I am. Will it really do to solve these paradoxes by saying that there are not only facts about what is actual but also about mere *possibilia*, and that it might have been that all facts about me were facts about a mere *possibile*? The system Q, interpreted as an ordinary modal logic, offers a way of keeping the clear definition of '*x* exists' as 'There are facts about *x*', and breaking the chain at another point. That it should be a fact that I do not exist—that it should be a fact that there are no facts about me— really is an impossible supposition; $NMN\Sigma\phi\phi x$ ought to be, and in the system Q is, a modal theorem. But $L\Sigma\phi\phi x$, that my existence is necessary, does not follow, if NMN does not entail L.

The system Q, considered as a logic of necessity and possibility, certainly has its own oddities, but a little reflection will usually find their justification. For example, one formula falsified by the tables is $CMpMApq$, 'If p is possible, either-p-or-q is possible'. Surely, one would think, the possibility of the disjunct p entails the possibility of the disjunction Apq. But let p be 'Only God exists', and suppose this possible, and let q be 'I don't exist'. Here p is possible *ex hypothesi*, but could the disjunction 'Either p or q', i.e.

'Either only God exists or I don't exist',

possibly be true? The peculiarity of it is that the disjunction is unstatable unless I exist, and is therefore only statable if both parts of it, 'I don't exist' and 'Only God exists', are false. In this case, then, 'Possibly either p or q' is false although 'Possibly p' is true. For the formula in its tense-logical interpretation the same counter-example could be used, with the hypothesis that at one time it was true that only God existed. Then 'At some time p' is true; but 'At some time either p or q' is not; for 'Either only God exists or I don't exist' is only statable when I do exist, and then both parts of it are false. The values of p and q which refute $CMpMAqp$ by the tables are 4 for p and 5 for q— $CM4MA45 = CM4M5 = C15 = 5$. These are the cases in which p is false now but was true yesterday, and q is false now but was unstatable yesterday; that is, today p and q are both false, and the only time at which p was true was one at which q, and therefore the whole disjunction, was unstatable.

A much more serious objection to the system Q as an ordinary modal logic is simply the absence from it of the rule to infer $L\alpha$ from α. This is serious, at least, if we suppose that it is *logical* necessity which L is being used to symbolize. For if it is not logically necessary that α, how does it come about that α is laid down as a law of the system? How can logical necessity thus appear as a stronger and narrower notion than that of exemplifying a logical law? We can answer this, I think, by distinguishing between the conditions of a statement's truth and the conditions of its formulability. To be logically necessary a statement must not only be incapable of being false, but necessarily formulable. But a statement exemplifies a logical law so long as its *truth* is secured by its logical form alone, even if its *formulability* depends on what is usually a contingent matter, the existence of such objects as are directly referred to in it. This distinction is unavoidable, it seems to me, in a modal logic for contingent beings, which is what the system Q would be.

On the other hand, the system Q does not commit us, as Łukasiewicz's Ł-modal system would if we treated it as an ordinary modal logic, to the view that there are no true assertions of necessity at all. And this seems to me an advantage, for I would not wish to go as far as Łukasiewicz does here. For one thing, it seems to me rash to exclude outright the idea that there are necessary beings. Even if we leave theology out of account— and that also seems to me rash; there is too much unconscious theological fantasy in modern logic, and it needs 'de-mythologizing'—there is much to be said for the view that the existence of numbers is necessary, and I suspect that one reason why the common modal systems have passed muster as long as they have is that people have thought of the statements involved as being primarily statements about such objects as numbers, or perhaps points in space, the existence of which can be assumed almost on logical grounds. But putting this too on one side, I can see no objection to saying that it is necessary that if something is a logician then something is a logician. I would deny, though, that the formula $LC\Sigma x\phi x\Sigma x\phi x$ expresses a logical law, since ϕx could stand here not only for 'x is a logician' but also for, let us say, 'x is a better logician than I am', and the statement 'It is necessary that if someone is a better logician than I am then someone is a better logician than I am' is false because there need not have been any me.

To group together those true statements (apart from ones about necessary beings) which begin with *L*, it would seem necessary to introduce special propositional and predicate variables for which it is not permissible to substitute either expressions containing free name-variables or expressions for which we may substitute expressions containing free name-variables. These special variables would be substitutable in theses for ordinary propositional and predicate variables, but the ordinary variables would not be substitutable for the special ones.[1] When we are driven to measures like this, however, we cannot help feeling that 'there must be an easier way'—the thing is getting too like the cycles and epicycles of the pre-Copernicans—and I hope later to do something to justify this feeling. The problem to be solved here, it should be noted, is only an aesthetic one—the system at this point becomes a little clumsy; that is all—and it should also be noted that the same problem arises when the system Q is used as a tense-logic; the problem, I mean, of grouping together those true statements which begin with L, now read as 'It is at all times the case that'. There is a graver problem in modal logic which even the system Q does not solve, though the analogous tense-logical problem can be solved with comparative ease.

Using the system Q, it has been possible to give a precise and consistent logical form to the statement that something which in fact does exist might not have done so; but I do not quite know how to do this with the statement that something might have existed which in fact does not, though it is easy to give a precise form to what could be a consequence of this—that even if in fact there is nothing which can ϕ, it nevertheless could be that something ϕ's. Just how *would* we express precisely and consistently, and without any mythology about *possibilia*, the belief that in some possible states of affairs there could be objects which in the actual state of affairs there are not? If the actual state of affairs were an entity which could be referred to by a proper name, say *a*, this proper name referring in all possible states of affairs to the same one possible state of affairs, we could no doubt express what we want to by some such form as

---

[1] For a fuller description of a different use of this device of variables with a restricted range, see Appendix C.

For some state-of-affairs *w*, it is the case in *w* that there is an *x* such that it is not the case in *a* that *x* exists.

But the idea that possible states of affairs are entities capable of being referred to by proper names is almost as mythological as the notion of *possibilia* or possible-individuals, which we have resolved from the start to avoid. We might perhaps exchange this for the myth that there could be a complete list A, B, C, etc., of all actual individuals, and then say that it is possible that there should be an *x* such that *x* is not identical with any of A, B, C, etc. But even apart from metaphysical objections, this device will only do to express the assumption that there might have been other individuals *besides* the ones there are; it will not enable us to express the assumption that there might have been others *instead of* the ones there are. For these would not be individuals of which it would be true that they were other than A, B, C, etc., for in the world supposed there would be no facts at all concerning A, B, C, etc.

On the other hand, to convey, without assuming that there already in some sense 'are' merely-future individuals, the idea that there will be individuals that there are not now, we need only say

For some *n*, it will be the case *n* days hence that there is an *x* such that it was not the case *n* days back that *x* exists.

There can be no comparable handling of the corresponding modal case, because there is no modal analogy to the *order* in which past and future times are arranged about the present time. Possible states of affairs are no more arranged in such an order about the actual state of affairs, than they are capable of being given proper names. The difficulty is, in short, that the non-existence of an object at some time or in some state of affairs can only be referred to *from* the time at which, or state of affairs in which, the object *does* exist; and whereas we can say exactly how the time now present would be identified *from* some other time, we cannot say how the state of affairs which happens to be the actual one would be identified *from* some other possible state of affairs, and I do not know that we can be said to 'identify' possible states of affairs anyway.

NOTE.—In a letter of 20 January 1956, a few weeks before his death, Łukasiewicz made the following comment on this lecture:

'It is evident that your 6-valued matrix of Q (and, as I suppose, your infinitely-valued matrix) does not verify the rule of detachment. This is a defect which cannot be avoided, and I think therefore that your system Q is defective too.

'I know, however, that such "irregular" matrices, i.e. matrices which do not verify the rule of detachment, are sometimes useful for proofs of independence. Such matrices were studied in my seminar in Warsaw before the war, and I shall give you here a simple example which may become useful for your further investigations.

'Let a fragment of the *C-N-p* classical calculus be defined by the matrix M:

C	I	2	3	N
*I	I	I	3	3
2	I	I	I	I
3	I	I	I	I

M

M is irregular, because we have $C12 = 1$. We can easily prove by this matrix that the principle of syllogism is independent from the law of Clavius and Duns Scotus. The equality $C12 = 1$ does not lead to odd consequences, as 2 cannot be defined in the system ($1 = Cpp$, $3 = NCpp$). Only a variable can have in this system the value 2. Now, if α is asserted, i.e. $\alpha = 1$, and β is a variable, we can always put for $\beta = 3$, getting from $C\alpha\beta = C13$ $= 3$. We see therefore that α and $C\alpha\beta$, when β is a variable, cannot be together asserted, so that the rule of detachment is also verified in this case, but in vacuo.

'The system defined by the matrix M is functionally not complete, i.e. not all functors which may be constructed by C and N (and 1, 2, 3) are definable by C and N. If we want to have a complete system, we must add new functors. Now, any new functor of one argument, say H, whose truth-value for the argument 1 is 2, i.e. $H1 = 2$, leads to a contradiction, if added to the system. If $H1 = 2$, then $HCpp = H1 = 2$, and $CCppHCpp = C12 = 1$. From Cpp and $CCppHCpp$ we get by detachment

$HCpp$, and $CHCppq = C2q = 1$; consequently we get q, a contradiction.

'It seems to me that any irregular matrix contains potentially a contradiction and I think for this reason that it is always dangerous to use such matrices as models of systems.'

It is fairly clear that our matrix for Q, like the simpler matrix M in Łukasiewicz's letter, only verifies the rule of detachment by being functionally incomplete. For example, we cannot define within it (i.e. define in terms of the N, K, M, and L which are the sole primitive operators of the system) a function of p whose sequence will have a 1 or a 3 where the sequence for p has a 2. Nor, with the intuitive interpretation given for the system, could any such function be given a meaning. Dr. Alan Ross Anderson has pointed out to me, however, that Q can be shown to be 'semantically complete' in the sense of S. Halldén,[1] i.e. it contains no theses of the form $A\alpha\beta$ in which α and β have no variables in common and yet neither is a thesis on its own.

---

[1] S. Halldén, 'On the Semantic Non-completeness of Certain Lewis Calculi', *Journal of Symbolic Logic*, xiv (1951), pp. 127–9.

VI

Modal Logic in the Style of Frege

UP to this point, I have drawn freely and uncritically upon a theory of quantification which may be broadly described as Russellian, with the typical Russellian apparatus of logical proper names, predicates, and descriptions. It must be admitted, however, that this kind of logic is at present a little out of fashion; and while I do not think this is anything to be taken at all seriously, it would unquestionably be of interest to see how some of the problems I have been discussing would appear if some different approach were adopted. In particular, it is worth seeing what happens if, instead of taking our cue from Russell, we take it from Frege. I do not, indeed, propose to develop a tense-logic in the manner of Frege, but I want to do something of the sort with ordinary modal logic, and the principles thus unearthed can be extended and adapted to tense-logic in ways which should by now be obvious. And as a preliminary, I wish to say one or two things about Frege's logic generally.

The theory with which Frege's name is especially associated is one which is apt to strike one at first as rather fantastic, being usually expressed as a theory that sentences are names of truth-values. I do not think it is watering down Frege's actual viewpoint, and it certainly makes it less puzzling, if we consider him to be discussing not sentences but the corresponding 'that' clauses—'That Caesar conquered Gaul', 'That Pegasus is white', and so on. These already look much more like names, and they are equivalent to phrases like 'The conquest of Gaul by Caesar', 'The whiteness of Pegasus', and so on, which look more name-like still. 'The True' and 'the False' are certainly quaint-sounding objects to be named by phrases like 'The conquest of Gaul by Caesar' or indeed by anything else; but perhaps we can think of 'the True' as simply 'the Truth', the totality of facts, and as for 'the False', Mr. R. J. Butler[1] has suggested that if we think of 'naming the True' as a kind of pointing at the

[1] Adapting a theory of Wittgenstein and Russell.

truth, we might think of 'naming the False' as a pointing directly away from the Truth. These aids to intuition are not, however, important; the main point is that when a statement is true, Frege thinks of the corresponding 'that'-clause as normally a name for the True, and when the statement is false, the corresponding 'that'-clause is normally a name for the false.

On Frege's view, then, the expression 'That Caesar conquered Gaul' is in ordinary contexts a name of the True or the Truth, and the expression 'That 2 and 2 are 4' is another name of the same object, just as 'The Morning Star' and 'The Evening Star' are two names for the same object. Of course these phrases 'The Morning Star' and 'The Evening Star', while naming the same object, are not only different phrases but have a different sense or meaning, and this is still more obviously the case with the names 'That Caesar conquered Gaul' and 'That 2 and 2 are 4', and in some contexts it is this sense or meaning which is named by the phrase or clause, rather than what it ordinarily names— the Truth, or Venus, or whatever it might be. Frege considers in this connexion the example of indirect speech. That 2 and 2 are 4 might be believed by someone who does not believe that Caesar conquered Gaul; but if in this statement the phrases 'That 2 and 2 are 4' and 'That Caesar conquered Gaul' refer to the same object, we would be ascribing contradictory attributes to this one object—being believed by X, and not being believed by X. In this context, therefore, what is being spoken about is not a truth-value but the senses of the expressions concerned, and these senses are of course different. Professor Church has suggested,[1] and in this as in much else we shall follow him, that this happens in modal contexts also. In the expression

'The necessity that Church is Church',

or in other words

'The necessity of Church's being Church',

the internal 'that'-clause is being used not as a name for the Truth but as a name for what is ordinarily the *sense* of this 'that'-clause. The expression as a whole, however, is in normal contexts a name for a truth-value, perhaps for the Truth.

[1] A. Church, 'A Formulation of the Logic of Sense and Denotation', in *Structure, Method and Meaning* (1951).

The point would be clearer if we used a different notation, e.g. if we put everything into capitals, when an expression is used to name what is normally its sense.[1] We may then say that the expression 'CHURCH'S BEING CHURCH' names the sense of the expression 'Church's being Church', which in turn is a name of the Truth. The operator 'That — is necessary' or 'The necessity of —', in Church's view, constructs a name of a truth-value, not out of another name of a truth-value, but out of a name of a sense, so that we ought to write 'The necessity of CHURCH'S BEING CHURCH' for the above name-of-a-truth-value.

One minor by-product of this way of doing things is that the resulting logic of necessity is not a modal logic in the sense of Łukasiewicz. For the things that do duty for statements in Frege's logic are names of truth-values, so that what would correspond in this logic to a statement-forming operator on statements would be an operator forming names of truth-values out of names of truth-values; and Church's necessity-operator is not an operator of this sort, since it forms names of truth-values, not out of names of truth-values, but out of names of the senses of names of truth-values. This might, however, be countered by a more liberal theory as to what we may regard in a logic of this type as corresponding to a statement. A more substantial point is that Church's system contains no law of the form $CLpp$, or even of the form $CLPp$, in which big-P names the sense of little-p. What it does contain may be explained as follows: Church says that the sense of an expression is a *concept* of the thing named by the expression; for example, THE MORNING STAR is a concept of the Morning Star, and THE EVENING STAR is another concept of this same Morning Star, i.e. of Venus, and THE CONQUEST OF GAUL BY CAESAR is a concept of the conquest of Gaul by Caesar, that is, of the Truth, while CHURCH'S BEING CHURCH is another concept of this same object, the Truth. And suppose we use the form ΔPp to mean that P is a concept of p. Then the nearest that Church comes to the law $CLpp$ is the law $C\Delta PpCLPp$, 'If P is a concept of p, then the necessity of P implies p'.

This formal point, however, we can ignore, though it is of interest as showing that even the first part of Łukasiewicz's definition of 'modal', though on most sides broader, is on this side narrower than ordinary usage. We have here at least a quasi-modal system, and we can proceed to consider what problems arise in it. Let us consider, in particular, a variation of our original example, namely the expression 'The necessity of PEGASUS'S BEING PEGASUS'. This example brings out the main difference between Frege's method of referring to individuals and Russell's. In Frege's system the distinction between logical proper names and singular descriptions vanishes. He has no expressions whose function is *solely* to identify a particular individual; all names are descriptions in so far as they have a sense, and sentences containing them also have a sense, and the same sense, whether the names have any reference or not. There can be no question, therefore, of making statements which in some other possible state of affairs could not be made at all. On the other hand, descriptions resemble proper names in that sentences containing them, though they have a sense, have no truth-value if the names have no reference. This is simply a special case of the general rule that if any name has no reference, then no larger name into which it enters has any reference either. Hence, since the name 'Pegasus' has no reference, the expression 'The tail of Pegasus' has no reference either, and neither does the expression 'Pegasus's being Pegasus', or 'That Pegasus is Pegasus'. These all have a sense, however, so that in the expression 'The necessity of PEGASUS'S BEING PEGASUS' the last part does name something, and so the whole names something too; and although what the part names is not a truth-value but a sense, what the whole names *is* a truth-value. But which one? *Is* PEGASUS'S BEING PEGASUS necessary?

In favour of a negative answer, we may ask how the sense of 'Pegasus's being Pegasus' could be a necessary sense if 'Pegasus is Pegasus' is not true. But if on these grounds we deny that PEGASUS'S BEING PEGASUS is necessary, can we admit that even CHURCH'S BEING CHURCH is necessary, for the expression 'Church is Church' *could be* without a truth-value, unless Church is a necessary being. It may be that this logic ought to have a structure like our system Q, in which 'The impossibility of PEGASUS'S NOT BEING PEGASUS' and 'The impossibility of CHURCH'S NOT BEING CHURCH' both name the True, while 'The necessity of PEGASUS'S BEING PEGASUS' and 'The necessity of CHURCH'S BEING CHURCH' both name the False.

This is not, however, a reason for denying that the statements 'Pegasus is Pegasus' and 'Church is Church' are exemplifications of a logical law. For if we admit truth-valueless sentences into our system at all, it seems hardly avoidable that some logical laws should have truth-valueless exemplifications. There are truth-valueless sentences, for example, even of the form Cpp; for example 'If Pegasus is a horse then Pegasus is a horse'. In this system, it would seem, we must count a formula as expressing a law so long as it has no exemplifications which are false. This is again reminiscent of the system Q; and, as in that system, leads to the rejection of the rule $\alpha \rightarrow L\alpha$, or rather of the rule $\alpha \rightarrow C\Delta A\alpha LA$, 'From α, infer that if A is a concept of α then A is necessary'. This rule must be rejected, at all events, if a necessary concept must always be a concept of the True.

This type of modal logic, then, seems only to reproduce the complications of our system Q, besides having others of its own; and these others extend even farther than we have yet indicated. It was observed that even in Q the status of the rule of detachment is a little shaky; the most we can say is that it needs no restriction until we introduce name-constants. But in systems of Frege's type it is much easier to construct cases in which, just by their form, α and $C\alpha\beta$ are never false but at worst sometimes truth-valueless, while β is sometimes not merely truth-valueless but false. Such cases arise as soon as Frege's name-and-predicate mechanism is introduced, so that the rule of detachment requires restriction from then on. Truth-valuelessness lends itself much more readily than unformulability to the construction of this type of case; we can even construct forms of which the exemplifications are *always* truth-valueless (any containing $\iota x K\phi x N\phi x$, e.g. the quite general $\psi\iota x K\phi x N\phi x$, would do), but there would be a kind of contradiction in constructing a form of what is always unformulable.

To make clear exactly what is at issue, consider the following two cases, in one of which the rule of detachment would be harmless and in the other not: The formula $I\iota x\phi x\iota x\phi x$ expresses a law of the present system, being a substitution in the law of identity Ixx, which is always either true or truth-valueless. And the formula $CI\iota x\phi x\iota x\phi x\Sigma x I\iota x\phi x$, 'If the thing that ϕ's is the thing that ϕ's, then something is the thing that ϕ's', is similarly always either true or truth-valueless. From these two we could

obtain by detachment $\Sigma x I x \iota x \phi x$, 'Something is the thing that
ϕ's', and this would not be objectionable, for although it seems
strange to say that 'Something is the round square' exemplifies
a logical law, this does not mean that it is true—since its component 'the round square' names nothing, it is truth-valueless,
and all statements of this form are either that or true. What
would be really awkward would be to have 'Something is *a*
round square', i.e. 'Something is at once round and square',
exemplifying a logical law, for this is not truth-valueless but
plain false. And this case we do have if we apply the rule of
detachment to $\phi \iota x \phi x$. 'The thing that ϕ's ϕ's' (e.g. 'The round
square is both round and square') and $C\phi \iota x \phi x \Sigma x \phi x$, 'If the thing
that ϕ's ϕ's then something ϕ's', both of which are never false
(even $C\phi \iota x \phi x \Sigma x \phi x$ is merely truth-valueless if its consequent is
false). Then again, by an unrestricted rule of detachment we
could pass from $\psi \iota x K \phi x N \phi x$ and $C\psi \iota x K \phi x N \phi x \psi \iota x \phi x$, both of
which are always truth-valueless, to $\psi \iota x \phi x$, which is in many
cases false.

A restriction which would leave us free to perform the detach-
ment leading to $\Sigma x I x \iota x \phi x$, but not those leading to $\Sigma x \phi x$ and to
$\psi \iota x \phi x$, would be one forbidding us to infer β from α and $C\alpha \beta$
when α contains an expression of the form $\iota x \phi x$ which does not
occur in β.[1] It would be worth investigating the conjecture that
the non-modal part of the theory of reference which Frege pre-
sented informally could be satisfactorily formalized on the following basis: To the classical propositional calculus and theory of
quantification add the usual pair of axioms for identity (Ixx and
$CIxyC\phi x\phi y$) and the following for descriptions:

1. $E\psi \iota x \phi x \Sigma x K \Pi y E \phi y I x y \psi x$.

2. $\phi \iota x \phi x$.

3. Rule: $N\alpha \rightarrow \psi \iota x \alpha$.

Detachment to take the form: α, $C\alpha\beta \rightarrow \beta$, provided that α contains no expression of the form $\iota x \alpha$ which does not occur in β.
Axiom 1 cannot be replaced by a definition, as this would
enable us to circumvent the restriction on detachment by employing definitional substitution, and so could lead to contradiction.

---

[1] Cf. the similar restriction for Q with Russellian name-constants.

In Frege's own formal system these complications are avoided by the device of assigning a fixed artificial reference to expressions which would ordinarily be said to have none at all. What object is selected for this purpose is immaterial, so long as it can be proved to exist; the number 0, for example, would do. Using this example, the procedure is this: if exactly one thing ϕ's, then the phrase 'the thing that ϕ's' is taken to refer to this one thing, but if nothing ϕ's, or more than one thing ϕ's, the phrase 'the thing that ϕ's' is taken to refer to the number 0. In this way genuinely non-referring names and truth-valueless statements are excluded from the scope of the system. A formal result of this device is that the law of identity Ixx yields true statements with all concrete substitutions for x, even the substitution 'The round square', for 'The round square is identical with the round square' is taken as simply a way of saying that the number 0 is identical with the number 0. Another formal result of the same device is that the formula $\phi\iota x\phi x$, 'The thing that ϕ's ϕ's', does *not* express a logical law, for such exemplifications of this form as 'The round square is both round and square' become ways of saying that the number 0 is both round and square, which is simply false. Hence no harm results if the rule of detachment is used without restriction.

Church, in his modal extension of Frege's system, takes over this procedure, with considerable consequent simplification. He admits in a footnote, however, that this is merely a way of keeping the difficult cases out of the discussion, and that it ought to be possible to construct a system in which non-referring names are admitted *as* non-referring. He also surmises that in such a system it would be necessary to modify ordinary quantification theory, but our earlier reasoning suggests that the modification of our ordinary assumptions is required at a slightly different point, though it is not required until names and predicates are introduced. I see no reason why, for instance, the law $C\phi y\Sigma x\phi x$ should not be retained, even though it has such substitutions as $C\phi\iota x\phi x\Sigma x\phi x$, provided that detachment is suitably restricted.

If we could tolerate all these complications, and if we could also tolerate on the philosophical side the view that every name must have a sense—the view, in other words, that we cannot use an expression *merely* to identify—would we reap any compensating advantages? We would gain, I think, this much: we *would* have a precise and consistent way of saying that there might have been things which in fact there are not, without bringing in *possibilia*. For we could say for this simply 'There is an X such that X is a possible concept although there is no x such that X is a concept of x'. In interpreting this, we should remember that concepts, as this term is used by Church, are the senses of denoting expressions such as 'The Morning Star' or 'The Pegasizer'; they are not possible-things, nor are they properties, a property being rather the sense of an expression like 'is a Morning Star', 'is a Pegasizer'. Hence the form just given does not mean 'There are possible-things which are not actual', which is metaphysically more than we want, nor does it mean 'There are properties which objects could have though none do', which is metaphysically less than we want. Whether the form gives exactly what we want is not clear to me; but Frege's logic at least has the merit of providing us with a form of statement, with a precise logic of its own, which at this point avoids two things which we do want to avoid.

On the other hand, following Frege will definitely not solve, so far as I can see, the aesthetic problem of symbolizing the common form of whole classes of statements which are either necessarily or at all times true, without introducing special variables with a restricted range. There are, however, other alternatives to the Russellian name-and-predicate mechanism beside this one; and at least one of them, the 'ontology' of Leśniewski, does seem to have something substantial to offer us at this point.

VII

Proper-name Logic and Common-noun Logic

THE system of quantified tense-logic in which the tense-logical system Q is combined with the Russellian name-and-predicate calculus I propose to call ΣT_1, and my aim now is to compare this with what I shall call ΣT_2, in which an appropriate tense-logic is geared to a modification of Leśniewski's ontology.[1] In developing this comparison I shall refer also to ordinary modal logic, and to another branch of logic too, but it will be convenient to make the consideration of tense-logic central.

A distinguishing feature of ΣT_1 is that it admits logical proper names only for objects which have present existence, and regards statements containing such names as incapable of being made except when those objects exist. In a system guided by Frege's logic of sense and denotation such statements would be regarded as always having a sense but not always a truth-value. In what I am calling ΣT_2, any expression which makes a statement at any time makes a statement at all times, and one with a truth-value too; and this result is achieved without modifying quantification theory and without committing ourselves to the sempiternity of all individuals.

Both the strength and the weakness of ΣT_2—for we shall find that it has weaknesses too—spring from its peculiarly indirect way of achieving individual reference in its statements. It contains no symbols for proper names and none for singular descriptions either, but it contains symbols for common nouns—we shall use the variables a, b, c, etc.—and symbol-sequences for singular statements, of the form ϵab. ϵab may be read 'The a is a b'. Note that for this to make sense, the terms a and b must be common nouns (though they could be ones like 'bucephalizer', artificially concocted out of proper names in the manner of Quine); and note that there is no symbol for 'The a'; a by itself

---

[1] See, on this, my *Formal Logic* (1955), III. iii. 4, and works there cited; also C. Lejewski, 'Logic and Existence', *British Journal for the Philosophy of Science*, August 1954; J. Słupecki, 'St. Leśniewski's Calculus of Names', *Studia Logica*, iii (1955); and my 'Definitions, Rules and Axioms', *Proceedings of the Aristotelian Society*, 1955-6, pp. 199 ff.

does not stand for an expression of this form, and the operator ϵ does not mean simply 'The . . .' but 'The . . . is a . . .', which is not further analysed. This is not as different as it looks from the Russellian procedure; Russell has the form $\imath x\phi x$ for 'The ϕ-er', but he does not define $\imath x\phi x$, but only gives equivalents for the main contexts in which it occurs. And Leśniewski has the following law:

$$E(\epsilon ab)(KK\Sigma c\epsilon ca\Pi cdCK\epsilon cae da\epsilon cd\Pi cC\epsilon ca\epsilon cb),$$

which asserts in effect that the a is a b if and only if (1) at least one thing is an a, (2) at most one thing is an a, and (3) whatever is an a is a b. This is reminiscent of the three parts of the Russellian definition of $\psi(\imath x\phi x)$, 'The ϕ-er ψ's'; but the Leśniewskian law is not a definition. It is not even a definition in the Leśniewskian sense, according to which a definition is a particular sort of axiomatic equivalence. This is an equivalence, but it is not that sort of equivalence, for the symbol ϵ occurs on both sides of it. For example, the part of the right-hand side which we have translated as 'At least one thing is an a', would be more strictly rendered as 'For some c, the c is an a', and the part which we have translated as 'Whatever is an a is a b' would be more strictly rendered as 'For all c, if the c is an a, the c is a b'.

The variables bound in this sort of formula are not, it should be emphasized, name-variables, but common-noun-variables. It is therefore misleading to translate, say, 'Σc' as 'There is an object c such that'. 'There is a kind-of-object c such that' would be more like it, but it is better to content ourselves with the simple 'For some c'. For even the translation 'There is a kind of object c such that' suggests that this kind-of-object is something which might *exist*, and this suggestion is misleading. These quantifiers, we might say, are like the English 'However' and 'Somehow' rather than the English 'Whatever' and 'Something'; we do not expand 'Somehow' to 'There is a how such that', and neither should we expand the Σc of this system in any such fashion. And 'Horse exists' is not a false but a senseless phrase. '*The* horse exists', however, is not; and the form 'The a exists' has a quite definite meaning in this system. It means 'For some c, the a is a c', and may be shortened to 'ob a'.

As in $\Sigma T1$, statements of the form $\Sigma\phi\phi a$ are true, and ones of the form $N\Sigma\phi\phi a$ are false, whenever they can be made, and if they can be made at any time they can be made at all times. Here they differ from the corresponding $\Sigma T1$ statements; in $\Sigma T2$, not only is $N\Sigma\phi\phi a$ always false, but so is $NPn\Sigma\phi\phi a$, 'It was not the case n days ago that for some ϕ, ϕa'. We have, in fact, $L\Sigma\phi\phi a$ as a law of the system; but remember that this does not mean 'a always exists' or even 'The a always exists'; it has no direct English translation, but it is equivalent to the statement that there is always some true statement in which the term a occurs. The true statement in question could be, among other things, the statement that the a does not exist. For in $\Sigma T2$ the statement 'The a does not exist', $N\Sigma\epsilon ac$, is not self-contradictory, and is sometimes true. It would be self-contradictory if it meant, or were equivalent to, the statement that there is no true statement in which the term a occurs; but it neither means nor is equivalent to this; what it is equivalent to is the statement that there is no true statement *of the form* ϵac into which the term a enters (it is not, of course, itself of this form); and what it means is that there is nothing which the a *is*.

The immense advantage of all this is that we can now regard the range of values for our bound variables as being fixed once and for all without being thereby committed to the view that all individuals are sempiternal, or—in modal contexts—that all individuals exist necessarily. For in this system to be a value of a variable is *not* the same thing as to be. We can therefore assent, without fear of awkward consequences, to the Barcan formula $CM\Sigma x\phi x\Sigma xM\phi x$, or as we would now write it $CM\Sigma a\phi a\Sigma aM\phi a$, both in its modal and in its tense-logical interpretation; to the simpler tense-logical formula $CF\Sigma a\phi a\Sigma aF\phi a$; to the rule 'From α, infer $L\alpha$', in both interpretations; to the equivalences of L and NMN and of M and NLN, in both interpretations; and to Łoś's axiom equating 'Not p-at-t' with 'Not-p at t'. We can in short now operate with our original S5-like tense-logic, which is what the system Q collapses into when from the sequences representing its 'truth-values' we delete all those containing any 2's.

Take, for example, the formula $CF\Sigma a\phi a\Sigma aF\phi a$. What this now asserts is that if it will be the case that for some a, ϕa, then for some a, it will be the case that ϕa. Note that I do not now read 'ϕa' as 'a ϕ's'. For expressions like 'Horse ϕ's' are senseless; ϕ here is not a verb, but any operator which constructs statements out of common nouns, such as 'The . . . does not exist', 'The . . . flies to the moon', 'The horse flies to the . . . ', and so on. The sort of thing that our antecedent could stand for is therefore 'it will be the case that for some c, the c flies to the moon', the consequent would then be 'For some c, it will be the case that the c flies to the moon', and this no more implies that what will fly to the moon now exists than the antecedent did.

These remarkable simplifications are, however, purchased at a cost. We begin to see what this cost is when we try to work out how we would distinguish between the case in which what will fly to the moon exists now, and the case in which it does not. At first it seems simple—when we affirm not only that it will be the case that something, say the c, flies to the moon, but also that this object now exists, we merely combine $F\epsilon ca$, 'It will be the case that the c is a moon-flyer', with the present-tense ob$c$, 'The c exists'; and in the other case we leave this latter portion out—it is a case of $Kobc F\epsilon ca$ on the one hand, and just $F\epsilon ca$ on the other. This is, in fact, the standard method of introducing complex terms into ontology without tense-operators. 'The c is a non-a', that is, 'The c is a thing-that-is-not-an-a', is equated with 'The c exists, and it is not the case that the c is an a', $Kobc N\epsilon ca$. Even the term 'thing-that-does-not-exist' is defined similarly—'The c is a thing-that-does-not-exist' is equated with 'The c exists, and it is not the case that the c exists'. This makes all statements of the form 'The c is a non-existent thing' self-contradictory and therefore false; but this result is entirely desirable, since if a is an empty term, that is, a term such that nothing is an a, any statement of the form 'The c is an a' *ought* to be false. (There is no contradiction, of course, about 'It is not the case that the c exists', which is *not* of this form.)

But does 'The c exists, and it will be the case that the c flies to the moon', $Kobc F\epsilon ca$, really assert all that we mean to assert when we say 'The c is (now) a thing-that-will-fly-to-the-moon'? Let c be the term 'President of the United States', so that the whole becomes 'The President of the United States exists, and it will be the case that the President of the United States flies to the moon'. But this could be true if it is one President who now exists, while it will be another President who flies to the moon. So not only is saying 'The President of the United States is an object-that-will-fly-to-the-moon', saying what is not said by 'It will be the case that the President of the United States flies to the moon', but we cannot bridge the gap between the two by adding 'The President of the United States exists' to the latter.

This type of problem arises in other fields also. Let us consider, for example, certain statements that might be made about two characters from my own country named Sid and Walter. In this logic, of course 'Sid' must be regarded as short for 'The Sidnifier' and 'Walter' similarly, but we need not dwell on that. The statements I have in mind are

(1) 'Sid believes that Walter's horse has wings', and

(2) 'Walter's horse is believed by Sid to have wings.'

These at first do not sound very different, but it is clear that the second implies that there is such an animal as Walter's horse, while the first does not. But even if we replace (1) by

(1)' 'Walter's horse exists, and Sid believes that Walter's horse has wings',

we still have something which could be true even though (2) is false. For suppose we took Sid to Walter's horse and said, 'Look—it has no wings after all', Sid might reply, 'Yes, *that* hasn't any—but that's not Walter's horse'. Then it would be true both that Walter's horse exists and that Sid believes that Walter's horse has wings, and yet false that Walter's horse is believed by Sid to have wings. What more do we need, then? Perhaps we might try adding

(3) 'Sid believes that Walter's horse is Walter's horse.'

But this would not do. For Sid might say, '*Of course* I believe that Walter's horse is Walter's horse—but that's not Walter's horse'. What we require is clearly not (3) but

(4) 'Walter's horse is believed by Sid to be Walter's horse.'

Add this to (1)', and you really do have something that implies (2). But this addition is itself of the form 'Walter's horse is believed to be a so-and-so', so there does not seem to be any way of reducing a statement of the form 'The c is believed to be a so-and-so' to a conjunction of statements of which none are themselves of that form. We therefore cannot *define* the complex term 'believed to be a so-and-so' in terms of the operator 'It is believed that', together with the notions of existence and identity, or in any other terms. And not only can we not say that 'It is believed that the *c* is a *d*' implies 'The *c* is a thing believed to be a *d*'; we cannot even say that 'The *c* is a thing believed to be a *d*' implies 'It is believed that the *c* is a *d*'; for the *c* may be believed-to-be-a-*d* by someone by whom it is not believed to be the *c*. Confronted with Walter's horse, perhaps dressed up by some students, Sid might believe that the object before him has wings, so that Walter's horse would be believed by Sid to have wings, even though he didn't believe that Walter's horse had wings.

The same difficulties would arise if we replaced 'Sid believes that' by 'It could be that' or 'It will be the case that'. 'It could be that Walter's horse has wings' does not imply that there is any such animal as Walter's horse, only that there could be; but 'Walter's horse is a thing that could have wings' does imply Walter's horse's existence. But the conjunction 'Walter's horse exists, and it could be that Walter's horse has wings' still does not imply 'Walter's horse is a thing that could have wings', for perhaps it can only be that Walter's horse has wings by Walter having a different horse. Nor does 'Walter's horse is a thing that could have wings' conversely imply 'It could be that Walter's horse has wings'; for it might be that Walter's horse could only have wings by not being Walter's horse. Similarly 'It will be the case that Walter's horse has wings' does not imply that Walter now has a horse, while 'Walter's horse is a thing that will have wings' does imply this; but 'Walter's horse exists, and it will be the case that Walter's horse has wings' is not sufficient to imply 'Walter's horse is a thing that will have wings', for it may be only after Walter has changed his horse that he will have one with wings. Moreover, 'Walter's horse is a thing that will have wings' does not imply 'It will be the case that Walter's horse has wings', for it may be that by the time Walter's horse acquires its wings it will have ceased to be Walter's horse.

And not only can we not assume that 'Walter's horse is a thing that will (could, is thought to) have wings' is equivalent to 'Walter's horse exists, and it will be (could be, is thought to be) the case that Walter's horse has wings'; we cannot assume that there is *anything* of the form 'Walter's horse is a so-and-so' which is equivalent to 'Walter's horse exists, and it will be (could be, is thought to be) the case that Walter's horse has wings'. To prove this we must make a considerable detour, but what we pick up on the way will have, I hope, its own interest.

To begin with, we may observe that the 'ontology' which enters into our $\Sigma T2$ cannot be quite exactly Leśniewski's,[1] since one of the features of Leśniewski's logic as a whole is that for each type of symbol we may lay down an appropriate 'law of extensionality', the one for ontology's ϵ being

(*a*) $C\Pi c E \epsilon c a \epsilon c b C \phi a \phi b$,

'If whatever is an *a* is a *b* and vice versa, then ϕa if and only if ϕb'. From this, given such operators as 'It could be that', 'It is believed that', 'It will be the case that', and using them to form functions of *a* and *b*, we could infer many obvious falsehoods. For example, let us suppose that a certain room is being used for a meeting of householders from Vernon Terrace, Christchurch, that all the householders turn up, and that there are no gate-crashers. Then every man in the room will be a householder of Vernon Terrace and vice versa; and by the above law of extensionality we could infer the following substitutions in $C\phi a \phi b$:

1. If something could be a man in this room without being a householder of Vernon Terrace, then something could be a householder of Vernon Terrace without being a householder of Vernon Terrace.

2. If it is believed that something is a man in this room without being a householder of Vernon Terrace, then it is believed that something is a householder of Vernon Terrace without being a householder of Vernon Terrace.

3. If it will be the case that something is a man in this room without being a householder of Vernon Terrace, then it will be the case that something is a householder of Vernon Terrace without being a householder of Vernon Terrace.

I do not think there is any need to be disturbed about this. Laws of extensionality serve, I would suggest, not so much to

---

[1] Where Leśniewski himself discusses time-distinctions in connexion with ontology, he deals with them in the Quine-Smart manner. See pp. 31–33 of Słupecki's 'St. Leśniewski's Calculus of Names', *Studia Logica*, iii (1955).

describe the world as to indicate the intended scope of a system. They are like the axiom *Iaa* ('Some *a* is an *a*') of Łukasiewicz's formalized syllogistic, which tells us not that there are no common nouns without application (which would be simply false) but that such nouns are not to be counted among the intended substitutions for the term-variables of the system. Similarly the Leśniewskian laws of extensionality tell us that non-extensional operators on terms are not among the intended substitutions for the ϕ's and ψ's of ontology; when such operators are introduced these laws must be dropped, just as *Iaa* must be dropped from any syllogistic system intended to apply to empty terms. Similarly if we believe in a third truth-value we will regard the law *ApNp*, 'Either *p* or not *p*', as an indication that the system in which it occurs is not intended to cover statements with this third truth-value, and must be dropped when the system is extended to take them in.

But it is not only the law (*a*) above which we must drop when non-extensional operators are introduced into ontology. We must also drop the weaker law of extensionality

(*b*) $CK\epsilon ab\epsilon baC\phi a\phi b$,

'If the *a* is a *b* and the *b* is an *a*, then if ϕa then ϕb'; that is, if the *a* and the *b* are the same object, then any propositional function of the term *a* implies that function of the term *b*. The standard examples with non-extensional functions of the terms 'Morning Star' and 'Evening Star' will suffice to falsify this. Although the Morning Star and the Evening Star are one and the same object, a man may believe that the Morning Star is the Morning Star without believing that the Evening Star is the Morning Star. As a consequence of the failure of this law (*b*) we cannot, in an ontology enriched with modal, temporal, or other non-extensional functions, equate 'The *a* is identical with the *b*', in the sense of 'The *a* is a *b* and the *b* is an *a*', with the form 'For all ϕ, if ϕa then ϕb'. Letting *a* stand for 'Morning Star' and *b* for 'Evening Star', we may read the first form as 'The Morning Star is the Evening Star' and the second as 'Morning Star is Evening Star'. The latter rendering is a little ungrammatical, but what it amounts to is that the terms 'Morning Star' and 'Evening Star' not only apply to the same object but have the same meaning. This is, of course, false, although 'The Morning

Star is the Evening Star' is true. On the other hand, 'Hydra is Hydra' is true, but 'The Hydra is the Hydra' is false, just as 'The Hydra is a Hydra' is false, because there is no Hydra. (The relation between the forms 'a is a', $\Pi\phi C\phi a\phi a$, and 'The a is the a', $K\epsilon a a\epsilon a a$, is thus like that between the forms $\Sigma\phi\phi a$ and $\Sigma c\epsilon a c$.) But in $\Sigma T\iota$ the form 'x is identical with y', where x and y stand for expressions which denote individual objects and mean what they denote—expressions whose sole purpose, in other words, is to identify an object, so that anything else they may happen to bring to mind is of purely psychological interest and is not part of what they are being used to say—'x is identical with y', in *this* sense, *is* equivalent to 'For all ϕ, if ϕx then ϕy'; and this has no awkward consequences, for such phrases as 'The Morning Star', 'The Evening Star', or 'The Hydra' are not permissible substitutions for x's and y's of this sort.

It may be useful at this point to summarize the resemblances and differences between the Russellian name-and-predicate logic, Frege's 'natural' name-logic, Frege's 'artificial' name-logic, and Leśniewski's ontology, by means of the following table:

	Russell	Frege (natural)	Frege (artificial)	Leśniewski
Substitutions permitted for name-variables	Singular expressions with denotation but no sense	Singular expressions with sense, with or without denotation	Singular expressions with sense; denotation always provided	Common nouns
Status of 'The ϕ-er' or 'The a'	Defined (in use); not substitutable for x	Undefined; substitutable for x	Undefined; substitutable for x	Not expressible
Status of 'The ϕ-er is a ψ-er' or 'The a is a b'	Defined	Defined	Defined	Undefined
Truth-value of preceding when nothing ϕ's, or is an a	False	None	Depends on denotation supplied	False
Status of 'x is x' or 'a is a'	Always true	Never false	Always true	Always true
Status of 'The ϕ-er is the ϕ-er' or 'The a is the a'	Sometimes false	Never false	Always true	Sometimes false
Status of 'The ϕ-er ϕ's' or 'The a is an a'	Sometimes false	Never false	Sometimes false	Sometimes false

(In the last three rows, 'Always true' means that all actual propositions of the given form are true, and 'Never' and 'Sometimes' are similarly understood.)

But the dropping of the law (b), $CK\epsilon ab\epsilon baC\phi a\phi b$, has a further consequence. To prove this law in Leśniewski's own system of ontology, it is not necessary to use the stronger law of extensionality (a); we only need the following three premisses:

(c) $C\epsilon aboba$.

(d) $CK\epsilon ab\epsilon bc\epsilon ac$.

(e) $E\epsilon a\lambda\phi K oba\phi a$.

Here (c) asserts that if the a is a b then the a exists, and (d) that if the a is a b and the b is a c then the a is a c; we can hardly question these even in a non-extensional ontology. In (e) it is assumed that the term $\lambda\phi$ has not occurred in the system before, and (e) is what Leśniewski calls an 'ontological definition' of $\lambda\phi$. By 'The a is a $\lambda\phi$' is meant 'The a exists, and ϕa'. Leśniewski's general permission to introduce such forms assumes that there is always *some* statement of the form 'The a is a so-and-so' which implies and is implied by 'The a exists, and ϕa'. For example, although it does not assume that 'Walter's horse is a thing that could have wings' is equivalent to 'Walter's horse exists, and it could be that Walter's horse has wings', it does assume that there is *something* of the form 'Walter's horse is a so-and-so' which is equivalent to the latter. And from this assumption, expressed in (e), together with the unobjectionable (c) and (d), we may deduce (b) as follows: 'The a is the b' $(K\epsilon ab\epsilon ba)$ entails 'The a is a b' (ϵab) and this entails 'The a exists' (oba), by (c). Hence 'The a is the b, and ϕa' entails 'The a exists, and ϕa'; and so, by (e), it entails 'The a is a $\lambda\phi$'. But 'The a is the b' also entails 'The b is an a'. Hence 'The a is the b, and ϕa' entails the two statements

'The b is an a',
'The a is a $\lambda\phi$',

from which we may infer 'The b is a $\lambda\phi$', by (d). But this is equivalent, by (e), to 'The b exists, and ϕb'. Hence 'The a is the b, and ϕa' entails ϕb; that is, if the a is the b, then if ϕa then ϕb; which is the law (b).[1] For example, let 'Walter's horse is a cheepy' be the defined equivalent of 'Walter's horse exists, and

---

[1] I owe this proof to Dr. B. Sobociński (in a letter of 16 Sept. 1953). It can now be found on p. 51 of Słupecki, op. cit.

Sid believes that Walter's horse has wings'. Then 'Walter's horse is this animal' implies 'Walter's horse exists', so that

'Walter's horse is this animal, and Sid believes that Walter's horse has wings'

implies

'Walter's horse exists, and Sid believes that Walter's horse has wings',

i.e. it implies 'Walter's horse is a cheepy'. But 'Walter's horse is this animal' also implies 'This animal is Walter's horse'; and from 'This animal is Walter's horse' and 'Walter's horse is a cheepy' we may infer 'This animal is a cheepy'. Hence from 'Walter's horse is this animal, and Sid believes that Walter's horse has wings' we may infer 'This animal is a cheepy', and so may infer 'Sid believes that this animal has wings'. To avoid this consequence we must deny that the conjunction 'Walter's horse exists, and Sid believes that Walter's horse has wings' is equivalent to anything at all of the form 'Walter's horse is a so-and-so' (say, 'cheepy').

It is clear, then, that in $\varSigma T2$ we need to have not only operators for forming temporally modified statements but also operators for forming temporally modified terms (like 'future President', 'former gamekeeper', 'perpetual mover'), neither type of operator being definable in terms of the other; and entailment relations between forms involving the two types must be stated with careful qualifications. Nor is this all. The logic of statement-forming tense-operators on statements is in $\varSigma T2$, as we have seen, of the comparatively simple S5 type; but the logic of term-forming tense-operators on terms cannot be so simple, but must be more like our system Q. To see this we need only consider the following facts. Though

(i) 'The a is a thing-that-will-be-a-b',

does not entail the form

(ii) 'It will be the case that the a is a b',

it does entail—as (ii) itself entails in another way—the form

(iii) 'It will be the case that for some c, the c is a b',

for even if the a ceases to be the a when it becomes a b, there will be some c such that the description 'The c' applies to it.

(Symbolically, we have $C\epsilon afbF\Sigma c\epsilon cb$, as well as $CF\epsilon abF\Sigma c\epsilon cb$, even though we have not $C\epsilon afbF\epsilon ab$.) Hence although the form

(iv) 'This a is a thing-that-will-be-non-existent'

does not entail the form

(v) 'It will be the case that the a is a non-exister',

it does entail the form

(vi) 'It will be the case that for some c, the c is a non-exister'.

But at no time can there be a c of which it is true to say 'the c is a non-exister'. Hence anything of the form (vi) must be false, and so, therefore, must anything of the entailing form (iv). Hence statements of the form 'The a is a thing-that-will-not-always-be existent', which are sometimes true, cannot be equivalent to statements of the (always false) form 'The a is a thing-that-will-be-non-existent'. But in a logic of the S5 type, the term 'thing-that-will-not-always-be-a-b' *would* be equivalent to 'thing-that-will-(at some time)-be-a-non-b'. Similar remarks may be made about terms subjected to ordinary modal qualifications. The term 'thing-that-need-not-be-a-b' cannot be equivalent to 'thing-that-could-be-a-non-b', since some things are things that need not be existent but nothing is a thing that could be-non-existent (i.e. be a non-exister).

Even if, in its details, the logic of tense-modified terms did not thus bring the complexities of the system Q into $\Sigma T2$ by the back door, the mere fact that $\Sigma T2$ has to have such a logic over and above that of tense-modified statements would be a complication; and it is a complication, moreover, which it is possible in $\Sigma T1$ to remove. For with variables standing for logical proper names, such as we have in $\Sigma T1$, we can reduce 'Walter's horse is a thing-that-will-have-wings' to 'There is an x such that x is Walter's only horse and it will be the case that x has wings', and 'It will be the case that Walter's horse has wings' to 'It will be the case that there is an x such that x is Walter's only horse and x has wings', thus making the necessary distinction without any extra machinery.

It must be added, however, that the translation into $\Sigma T1$ of what we might call the 'good' parts of $\Sigma T2$ is only possible if $\Sigma T1$ is enriched by special propositional and predicate variables of the sort mentioned when we were discussing modality; that is, by variables for which it is not permissible to substitute either expressions containing free variables or expressions for which it is permissible to substitute such expressions. For example, suppose we want to express in $\varSigma T{\scriptstyle 1}$ the law of $\varSigma T{\scriptstyle 2}$ $LC\epsilon ca\epsilon ca$, 'It is at all times the case that if the c is an a then the c is an a'. Remembering the Russellian account of definite descriptions, what would seem to correspond to this in $\varSigma T{\scriptstyle 1}$ would be 'It is at all times the case that if exactly one thing ϕ's and whatever ϕ's ψ's, then exactly one thing ϕ's and whatever ϕ's ψ's'. But this is not a law in $\varSigma T{\scriptstyle 1}$, for if we let the predicate ψ in the formula be 'treads on *this*', the result is not true, for it is not at all times the case that if exactly one thing ϕ's and whatever ϕ's treads on *this*, then exactly one thing ϕ's and whatever ϕ's treads on *this*. This is not the case, because once there were no facts at all about *this*. If, indeed, we replace the demonstrative by the descriptive phrase 'the thing now indicated by the Priorizer', and expand this in the Russellian manner, the result will be true; but we can only obtain a formula which will hold for all values of its variables, if the predicate-variables are of a kind which permit of the second type of replacement—the replacement of ψ by 'treads on the thing now indicated by the Priorizer'—but not of the first type of replacement. It must be admitted, therefore, that if the use of $\varSigma T{\scriptstyle 2}$ is beset with complications in certain 'bad' cases, the use of $\varSigma T{\scriptstyle 1}$ is beset with at least equal complications—complications of principle, so to speak, and not just complications of detail—in other cases. The best plan, I would like to suggest, is to imitate the methodological morals of the physicists and use $\varSigma T{\scriptstyle 2}$ on week-days and $\varSigma T{\scriptstyle 1}$ on Sundays.

$\varSigma T{\scriptstyle 1}$ and $\varSigma T{\scriptstyle 2}$ are not, however, the only alternatives open to us; there is also a system which I shall call $\varSigma T{\scriptstyle 3}$, derived like $\varSigma T{\scriptstyle 2}$ from Leśniewski's ontology, which is worth briefly sketching, though I have not explored it very far.

VIII

The Weak 'the' and the Strong 'the'

IN ordinary speech, with tenses, there are two senses of the word 'the' which we may describe as the weak 'the' and the strong 'the'. (In a Leśniewskian calculus, what we have to do with is more accurately a weak 'The — is a —' and a strong 'The — is a —'.) In the weak sense 'The a is a b' is true so long as an a is a b when it is the only a at the time of utterance. This is the 'the' which we use in common speech in phrases like 'The President of the United States'; and that is the sense we have given to ϵ in our system $\Sigma T2$. But in the strong sense, 'The a is a b' only if the a which is a b is the only a there is or has been or will be. In this sense of 'the', all statements to the effect that *the* President of the United States is something or other will be false, for there have been many Presidents of the United States. On the other hand, there will be, at least so long as Mr. Eisenhower exists, true statements to the effect that the 1955 President of the United States is something or other even when the 'the' intended is the strong one.

Both the weak and the strong 'the' are definable in $\Sigma T1$. In the weak sense, 'The ϕ-er is a ψ-er' is definable as

'For some x, x ψ's, x ϕ's, and whatever ϕ's is identical with x',

while in the strong sense it works out as

'For some x, x ψ's, x ϕ's, and whatever ϕ's, has ϕ'd, or will ϕ is identical with x'.

It is also possible to define the strong 'The — is a —' (we may write it as ϵ') in terms of the weak ϵ of $\Sigma T2$, though I am doubtful whether this can be done without tense-forming tense-operators on terms. In any case there is another and more interesting possibility, namely that of taking the strong ϵ' as undefined, and defining ϵ in terms of it. This is the characteristic feature of the system I shall call $\Sigma T3$.

Though I have not attempted to axiomatize either, it seems probable that a satisfactory axiomatization will be more difficult to find for $\Sigma T3$ than for $\Sigma T2$. It is clear, at all events, that the Leśniewskian axiom for ϵ, namely

A1. $E(\epsilon ab)(KK\Sigma c\epsilon ca\Pi cdCK\epsilon ca\epsilon da\epsilon cd\Pi cC\epsilon ca\epsilon cb)$,

must be dropped when ϵ is replaced throughout by ϵ'. For the right-hand side will not then entail the left. For example, if our $\epsilon'ab$ is '*The* President of the United States is a retired general' it is false, since there is no such person as *the* President, in this sense of 'the'; but the corresponding right-hand side assertion, that there is (now) one and only one President of the United States and whoever is (now) President of the United States is a retired general, is true.

A1 does, however, continue to hold if we replace ϵ by ϵ' on the right-hand side only, and the resulting equivalence gives us, in its right-hand side, a definition of the form ϵab in terms of ϵ'. And $\Sigma T3$ has some very substantial advantages. In particular, it is possible to lay down in $\Sigma T3$ a qualified law of extensionality, and with terms of a certain type it is possible to dispense with term-forming tense-operators on terms in favour of the corresponding operators on statements, by means of 'ontological definitions'. (This is an advantage because in $\Sigma T3$ as in $\Sigma T2$ we can use the comparatively simple S5 type of logic for tense-operators on statements, and retain the Barcan formula and Łoś's law equating $NUtp$ and $UtNp$.) For example, 'The 1984 President of the United States is one who will fly to the moon' *can* be equated with 'The 1984 President of the United States exists, and it will be the case that the 1984 President flies to the moon'.

This equation of $\epsilon'afb$ with $Kob'aF\epsilon'ab$ (where ob$'a = \Sigma b\epsilon'ab$), and in general of $\epsilon'a\lambda\phi$ with $Kob'a\phi a$, is not, however, always possible. For example, even if by '*The* horse of Walter' we mean the only horse that Walter has, has had, or will have, we still cannot equate 'Walter's horse is a thing that will have wings' with 'Walter's horse exists, and it will be the case that Walter's horse has wings'. For it is still possible that this unique horse of Walter's will only have wings after he has been sold to someone else, in which case it would be true that Walter's horse is a thing that will have wings and false that it will be the case that Walter's horse has wings. The equation of $\epsilon'a\lambda\phi$ with $Kob'a\phi a$ will in general hold only where a is the sort of term which, if it applies to an object at all, applies to it throughout the period of its existence. ('1984 President of the United States' is such a term if we take it to mean 'person who is, has been, or will be President of the United States for 1984'.)

Let us call terms of this sort 'permanent' terms. If we use the form πb to mean that b is a permanent term, we may define this form as follows:

$$\text{Df. } \pi : \pi b = \Pi t a C U t \epsilon' a b \Pi t C U t \text{ob}' a U t \epsilon' a b$$

('b is a permanent term' = 'For all t and a, if the a is a b at t then if the a exists at any time the a is a b at that time'). And with π thus defined we may lay down the following conditional law of extensionality for ϵ':

$$CK\pi a\pi bCK\epsilon' ab\epsilon' ba C\phi a\phi b.$$

'If a and b are permanent terms, then if the a is the b' (strong 'the') 'then any function of a implies that function of b'. We have seen in connexion with $\Sigma T2$ that it is only where a law of extensionality is applicable that 'ontological definitions' can be safely laid down.

Even this limited possibility of ontological definition in $\Sigma T3$ has far-reaching consequences. For example, it is possible to eliminate special tense-operators on terms from the predicates of ϵ-propositions by making use of the definition of ϵ in terms of ϵ' together with the relevant 'ontological' definitions. Without giving a full justification for the procedure, we may consider a few examples. 'Walter's horse is (ϵ) a thing-that-will-be-winged' can in $\Sigma T3$ be distinguished from 'It will be the case that Walter's horse is (ϵ) winged' by equating the one to

'For some c, the c is (ϵ') Walter's only present horse and it will be the case that the c is (ϵ') winged'

and the other to

'It will be the case that for some c, the c is (ϵ') Walter's only present horse and is (ϵ') winged'.

These are exactly analogous to the reductions of these two statements which are possible in $\Sigma T1$, with ϵ eliminated not in favour of ϵ' but in favour of functions of logical proper names. But the $\Sigma T3$ reductions have the advantage over the $\Sigma T1$ ones of not requiring the system Q, but only the S5 type of system, for the tense-logical operators on statements which remain after the reduction. For example, the two forms

(a) 'The *a* is (ϵ) a thing that is sometimes a non-exister'

and

(b) 'The *a* is (ϵ) a thing that is not always an exister'

expand first to

(a)' 'For some *c*, *c* is a permanent term, the *c* is (ϵ') the only present *a*, and *it is sometimes the case that the c is (ϵ') a non-exister*'

and

(b)' 'For some *c*, *c* is a permanent term, the *c* is (ϵ') the only present *a*, and *it is not always the case that the c is (ϵ') an exister*'.

Here the italicized portions themselves expand to

(a)'' 'It is sometimes the case that the *c* exists (ob'*c*) and the *c* does not exist'

and

(b)'' 'It is not always the case that (the *c* exists and) the *c* exists'.

(a)'' is in no case true, but (b)'' is true in some cases; so our analysis has shown how the original (a) is false even in cases for which (b) is true, and this has been done without assuming any difference in truth-value between 'Sometimes not-*p*' and 'Not always *p*'.

Whether distinctions like those made in Q are required at any point is $\Sigma T3$ I do not know. But it must be emphasized that we have the advantages of this system only if it is interpreted as being strictly tense-logical. If ordinary modal operators, or ones like 'It is believed that', enter into the ϕ of our ontological definition-form and of our conditional law of extensionality for ϵ', these cease to be acceptable. For example, even if 'Morning Star' and 'Evening Star' were permanent terms, the fact that the Morning Star is the Evening Star (strong 'the') would not warrant us in affirming that whatever is believed to be the Evening Star is believed to be the Morning Star.

We might, indeed, obtain conditional laws of extensionality (and all the rest) even in these fields if we strengthened our 'the' on the appropriate side—if, for example, we counted the form 'The a is a b' as true only if the a is not merely the only a there ever has been or will be but the only a there could be. But what on earth could we do with a system like this? When could it *not* be said, when we are confronted with something which we are inclined to describe as 'the' c, that there at least might have been something else which might have been a c? Possibly when it is God of whom we speak, but I cannot think of any other occasion. But we will be in a better position to consider this proposal when we have gone into the advantages of the strictly tense-logical $\Sigma T3$ a little farther.

$\Sigma T3$ comes closest, of all the systems we have yet considered, to the naïve logic of sempiternal 'objects' which from time to time acquire and lose 'existence'. It is not quite that; but we might well say that if a term a is such that there are or have been or will be true propositions of the form $\epsilon'ab$, then a is a 'proper name' (though not a 'logical proper name' in the sense of Russell) and the a is an 'identifiable individual'; although the a can only be said to 'exist' when there not merely have been or will be but *are* true propositions of the form $\epsilon'ab$. That is, we can define 'The a is an identifiable individual', by contrast with 'The a exists', as

$$\Sigma bAA\epsilon'abP\epsilon'abF\epsilon'ab,$$

or more briefly

$$\Sigma bM\epsilon'ab.$$

(We could do this with the weak ϵ too, but it would not give us what we want, for $\Sigma bM\epsilon ab$ would be true even if different objects were 'The a' at different times.) But we must be careful; in particular it must be observed that if we read the form $\Sigma bM\epsilon'ab$ as 'The a is an identifiable individual', the operator 'The — is a —' which occurs in this statement is *not* ϵ' (or of course ϵ); for nothing of the form $\epsilon'ab$ (or ϵab) is true when the a is not in actual existence. We might introduce a term i, meaning 'identifiable individual', by ontological definition, but the definition could not be

(i) $E(\epsilon'ai)(\Sigma bM\epsilon'ab),$

for if we could lay this down we could deduce the thesis of sempiternity in the crudest sense, for from (i) we could infer

(ii) $C(\Sigma b M\epsilon' ab)(\epsilon' ai)$,

and from this

(iii) $C(\Sigma b M\epsilon' ab)(\Sigma b\epsilon' ab)$,

i.e. if the a is-an-identifiable-individual (if it is or has been or will be the case that the a exists), then the a exists now. And if we employ an ontological definition of the proper form, that is

(iv) $E(\epsilon' ai)(Koba\Sigma b M\epsilon' ab)$,

we again equate 'The a is an identifiable individual' with 'The a exists' (for we equate it with 'The a exists, and it is, has been, or will be the case that the a exists', and the first conjunct of this implies the second), but now in a harmless way, for all that the result now means is that we have not succeeded in equating 'The a is (ϵ') an identifiable individual' with the thing we want. We can, however, define in terms of the ordinary ϵ' the 'is' which occurs in 'The a is an identifiable individual' in the sense intended; the definition is simply

$$\text{Df. } \epsilon'':\epsilon'' = M\epsilon'.$$

And we *can* then introduce the form $\epsilon'' ai$ as short for $\Sigma b\epsilon'' ab$. We cannot conversely define ϵ' in terms of ϵ'', or ob' in terms of i; we cannot equate 'being' in the full sense with 'being' (in the sense of ϵ'') some particular kind of thing—that is the difference between $\Sigma T3$ and what I have called the naïve object-existent system. But ϵ'' is an extremely useful operator all the same, for it can be associated with *numerical* quantifiers of an important kind.

We often want to say that exactly two things have ϕ'd, without committing ourselves either to the assertion that there now are exactly two things which at one time or another have been ϕ-ing or to the assertion that at some time or other it has been the case that exactly two things are ϕ-ing. That is, we want to say 'Exactly two things have ϕ'd' in a sense in which neither the existence nor the ϕ-ing of the two things need overlap. And such an assertion *can* be translated both into $\Sigma T1$ and into $\Sigma T2$, but the translation is difficult. We might think, for example, that in $\Sigma T2$ we could translate 'Exactly two things have been c's', in this sense, as

'For some a and b

(1) it has been the case that the a exists, and it has been the case that the b exists,

(2) it has never been the case that the a is the b, and

(3) it has always been the case that a thing is a c if and only if it is either the a or the b.'

But this will not do, if the weak 'the' of $\Sigma T2$ is what is intended; for (1) it has been the case that the President of the United States exists, and it has been the case that the Vice-President of the United States exists, (2) it has never been the case that the President is the Vice-President, and (3) it has always been the case that a thing is a President-or-Vice-President if and only if it is either the President or the Vice-President; but it is not true that there have been exactly two Presidents-or-Vice-Presidents of the United States—there have been dozens. If, however, the 'the' in the formula just given is the strong 'the' of $\Sigma T3$, it does give us what we require; and we can of course count future objects in the same way. Thus we can define the form $\Sigma(2)a\epsilon''ac$ to be read as 'Exactly two things are, have been, or will be c's' (in the sense intended) as follows:

Df. $I':I'ab = K\epsilon'ab\epsilon'ba.$

Df. $(2):\Sigma(2)a\epsilon''ac$
$$= \Sigma ab KK(K\epsilon''ai\epsilon''bi)(NMI'ab)(L\Pi dE\epsilon'dcAI'daI'db).$$

Operators $\Sigma(3)a$, $\Sigma(4)a$, etc., can be introduced in a similar way.

We can now return to the question of an analogue of $\Sigma T3$ in which L and M are given their ordinary modal significations. A great merit of $\Sigma T3$ as a tense-logic is that it gives an easy sense to the *counting* of individuals which do not now exist. We do often want to do just that; but do we want to count *possibilia* and *cogitabilia* in the same way? Do we want, when enumerating 'things that could be c's', to list objects that could exist but don't in the way that we do sometimes want, when enumerating things that have been c's, to list objects which have existed but exist no longer? So far as I can see we do not. We want to be able to say, and even in the modal analogue of $\Sigma T\iota$ we *are* able to say, that it could be that exactly two things are c's, and also that there are exactly two things which could be c's, but we do not want to say 'Exactly two things could be c's' in a sense in which one of the two things might be an actual thing and the other merely possible; and it is not at all clear that there *is* any such sense of 'Exactly two things could be c's'. Similarly the only intelligible senses of 'Exactly two things are thought to be c's' are 'It is thought that exactly two things are c's' and 'There are exactly two things which are thought to be c's'. There seems, therefore, to be nothing to be said for so strengthening 'the' that we could deny someone's right to talk about 'the' c on the ground that there could have been or are thought to be other c's although there are none in actual fact.

In one way, though, $\Sigma T3$ perhaps gives us too much. For it gives us not only identifiable former-individuals but also identifiable individuals-to-be, and these in some profusion—the things-that-will-be-c's are in all cases countable in principle in the same way as the things-that-have-been-c's. And some of us at least would like to see *futura*, or most of them, contrasted more sharply with *praeterita* and put in a position more like that of *possibilia* and *cogitabilia*. $\Sigma T3$ solves some of the problems about 'degrees of reality' that were raised in Chapter IV; we can distinguish now between 'The a is an object (identifiable individual)' and 'The a exists'; but past and future are still on a level, gaining together what they lost together in $\Sigma T\iota$. But this is a remediable defect, though we shall find that curing it is an arduous and intricate business, and here cannot be more than begun.

IX

Intentional Logic and Indeterminism

HAVING in mind the scholastic view that all mental acts have an intention or reference to an object, I propose to use the phrase 'intentional logic' for the study of statements formed by such operators as 'It is believed that', 'It is supposed that', 'It is desired that', 'It is feared that', 'It is asserted that'. We have already found a number of parallels between the problems arising in this subject and those arising in tense-logic and in ordinary modal logic; we have also just begun to notice what look like some differences, at least from tense-logic. And there is one apparent difference between intentional logic and tense-logic which I wish now to examine fairly fully. I shall assume, to begin with, that we are working with a name-and-predicate apparatus of the Russellian kind.

It is clear that the statement 'I believe that someone is eating fish and chips' does not imply 'There is someone who is believed by me to be eating fish and chips', just as 'It will be the case that someone is eating fish and chips' does not imply 'There is someone who will be eating fish and chips'. But it appeared that if we could assume that whoever will exist exists already, the statement 'It will be the case that someone is eating fish and chips' *does* imply 'There is someone who will be eating fish and chips'. To simplify the point, let us suppose that the universe contains only the two individuals A and B. And provided that we assume that these are not only all the individuals there are but all the individuals there will be, we can equate 'It will be the case that someone is ϕ-ing' with 'It will be the case that either A or B is ϕ-ing', and we can in any case equate 'There is someone who will be ϕ-ing' with 'Either A will be ϕ-ing or B will be ϕ-ing'. And 'It will be the case that either A or B is ϕ-ing' does seem to imply 'Either A will be ϕ-ing or B will be ϕ-ing'. But we cannot mend the corresponding inference in intentional logic in the same way, for even if we suppose that A and B are not only all the individuals there are but all the individuals I believe there are, so that 'I believe that someone is ϕ-ing' is equivalent to 'I believe that either A or B is ϕ-ing', this does not imply 'Either I believe that A is ϕ-ing or I believe that B is ϕ-ing', the equivalent under these conditions of 'There is someone whom I believe to be ϕ-ing'. For I might definitely believe that either A or B is ϕ-ing, but not have made up my mind as to which of them is doing it.

But once this apparent divergence between the two systems has been stated, we may well begin to wonder whether it is any more than apparent. May it not be that we have not hit upon a point at which tense-logic is really different from intentional logic, but rather upon a point at which our tense-logic needs to be revised?—just as, perhaps, what we are at first inclined to see as divergences between modal logic and tense-logic are really points at which modal logic needs to be revised. Is the inference

> It will be the case that either A or B is ϕ-ing,
> Therefore either A will be ϕ-ing or B will be ϕ-ing,

which has no parallel in intentional logic, really as good as it looks? Suppose A and B are being pushed towards the edge of a cliff, and there will be no stopping this process until there is only room for one of them. Then we may be able to say truly that it will definitely be the case that either A or B will fall over, even though we cannot say truly either that A will definitely fall over or that B will definitely fall over. And if there is a whole group of people being thus forced towards the edge, perhaps we can say truly that it will definitely be the case that someone will fall over, and yet that there is no one of whom it is definitely the case that *he* will fall over; and this may be true even though there is no question of persons yet unborn being brought into the situation before it ends. The key word here seems to be the word 'definitely', so let us introduce the symbol L for this (abandoning, of course, our earlier tense-logical use of L). We can then lay that $LF\Sigma x\phi x$ does not imply $\Sigma xLF\phi x$, even where there is no 'ampliation' of the range of values for the variable x.

But what have we added here by introducing this symbol L? In what way does 'x will definitely be ϕ-ing' differ from the plain 'x will be ϕ-ing'? Could 'x will be ϕ-ing' be true when 'x will definitely be ϕ-ing' is false? What could it mean to ϕ, or to be going to ϕ, indefinitely? I do not know that this could mean anything; but perhaps it could be not definitely true that x will ϕ, and also not definitely false. We are back now, of course, with Aristotle's future sea-battle. Suppose that the future is not wholly determined, and that it is still open to x to ϕ, and also open to x not to ϕ. Using the symbol M not for being at some time true, and not for the mere absence of logical inconsistency, but for this circumstance of having something still open to one, we may say that we have here both $MF\phi x$ and $MNF\phi x$. What is the truth-value under these circumstances of the simple statement that x will ϕ? We cannot say that it has none—that x is no longer or not yet mentionable, and the statement that x will ϕ therefore incapable of being made. And yet it is not now a *fact* that x will ϕ, nor is it now a fact that x will not ϕ; that is, the statement that x will ϕ is not now true, nor is it now false, even though there *is* such a statement. These considerations, unlike those raised in an earlier lecture, do involve us, it seems to me, in a denial of the law of excluded middle; in cases like this we must assign to the statement that x will ϕ the third or 'neuter' truth-value of Aristotle and Łukasiewicz (I mean the Łukasiewicz of the 1920's—later Łukasiewicz favoured a different system, the Ł-modal). On this view, the statement 'x will ϕ' is definitely true only when the statement 'x will definitely ϕ', or 'It is not now open to x not to ϕ', is true (and there is no other truth but definite truth); but the statement 'x will definitely ϕ' is not false only when the simple 'x will ϕ' is false; it is also false—definitely false, of course—when it is still open to x both to ϕ and not to ϕ; that is, when 'x will ϕ' is not true or false but neuter. So the symbol L as here used is not a redundant one; when p is true or false, p and Lp (p and 'Definitely p') have the same truth-value, but when p is neuter in truth-value, Lp is false.

Just this, so far as I can see, is what is forgotten in the Diodoran proof that whatever is possible, in the sense of being an alternative that is still open, either is or will be true. I have discussed this so-called Master Argument of Diodorus elsewhere[1] but it is worth introducing again to develop this point. The known premisses of the argument are these: (1) that whatever has been the case cannot now not have been the case (that is, the possibility of its not having been the case is not now open), and (2) that whatever definitely implies an impossibility is itself

[1] In 'Diodoran Modalities', *Philosophical Quarterly*, July 1955, Part II.

impossible. The premisses not now known are, I suspect, the following: (3) that anything's being the case definitely implies that it has not been the case that it will never be the case; and (4) that if anything now neither is nor will ever be the case, then it has by now been the case that it will never be the case. These premisses are, at all events, ones which have an appearance of truth and which would, along with the known premisses, yield the Diodoran conclusion. For let us suppose, as one of the opponents of Diodorus did, that there is a shell at the bottom of some shallow water which neither is nor ever will be seen, and let us see if we can consistently suppose that it nevertheless *can* be seen. Since it neither is nor ever will be seen, it has been the case that it will never be seen. Hence, by the first Diodoran premiss, it cannot now not have been the case that it will never be seen. That is, it is now *impossible* for it not to have been the case that it will never be seen, and by Diodorus' second premiss, anything that implies this impossibility is itself impossible. But the supposition that the shell is being seen *would* imply that it has not been the case that the shell will never be seen; this supposition is therefore an impossible one. That is, it is *not* possible that the shell should now be seen, or, to say that it *can* now be seen is not true. And in the same way it may be shown in any other case that if x neither is or will be ϕ-ing, it is not possible for x to ϕ.

Given what I surmise to be Diodorus' premisses, his conclusion certainly follows, and, moreover, in the case just considered it is not really unreasonable. We have supposed that it is definitely false that the shell either is or will be seen, and if this is so it *is* false that the possibility of being seen is now open to it. Conversely, if the possibility of being seen *is* now open to the shell, then it cannot be false that the shell either is or will be seen. It does not follow, however, that it must be true; it may be neuter. And this possibility is overlooked also in what I have surmised to be Diodorus's fourth premiss, that if anything neither is nor ever will be the case, then it has been the case that it will never be the case. If it is definitely true that the shell neither is nor ever will be seen, then it has definitely come to pass, so to speak, that the shell is not and never will be seen. And if this has not definitely come to pass, then it cannot be definitely true that the shell neither is nor will be seen. But it may not be definitely false either, it may be neuter. So the implication 'If x neither is nor ever will be ϕ-ing, then it has been the case that x will never be ϕ-ing', could have a neuter antecedent and a false consequent, and in that case the implication as a whole, by Łukasiewicz's table, would not be true but neuter. We cannot, therefore, lay down this implication as a logical law, and the 'Master Argument' fails.

Turning to a more recent controversy, we are committed by this view to maintaining the 8th of the theses condemned by Kilwardby at Oxford in 1277 that *every true proposition in the future tense is necessary*;[1] for only what is already necessary ('definite') can be properly said to be already true. It does not follow, however, either that future-tense propositions which are *not* necessary are false (they may be neuter), or that all propositions of the form 'If it will be the case that p, then it will necessarily be the case that p' are true (for if Fp here is neuter, LFp will be false, and $C23 = 2$). And there are other senses of 'necessary' (e.g. logically necessary) in which there are not only true propositions about the future but also true propositions about the past which are not necessary.

The effect of the 3-valued view on quantified formulae is a little complicated. Let us suppose, as before, that it definitely will be the case that something ϕ's, but that there is nothing of which it definitely will or definitely will not be the case that it ϕ's. We are supposing, that is to say, that $LF\Sigma x\phi x$ is true and $\Sigma x LF\phi x$ is false. In this case the simple $F\Sigma x\phi x$, 'It will be the case that something ϕ's', will also be true, for what will definitely be the case will be the case. But will the simple $\Sigma x F\phi x$, 'There is something which will ϕ', be false, neuter, or even true? There is no one answer to this, because in many-valued logics there are different operators which resemble in different ways the existential quantifier of two-valued logic, and which therefore have a claim to be represented by the symbol Σ. But if we wish to preserve in association with Łukasiewicz's 3-valued implication his two usual rules for the existential quantifier—that if $C\phi x\beta$ is a law, so is $C\Sigma x\phi x\beta$, provided that x does not occur freely in β, and that if $C\alpha\phi x$ is a law, so is $C\alpha\Sigma x\phi x$—our 3-valued Σ will have to have the following properties: (1) If, for a given

[1] J. Isaac, *Le Péri Herméneias en occident de Boèce à Saint Thomas* (Paris, 1949), pp. 124, 176.

ϕ, at least one statement of the form ϕx is true, 'Something ϕ's' is true; (2) if our ϕ is such that all statements of the form ϕx are false, 'Something ϕ's' is false; and (3) with all other kinds of ϕ, 'Something ϕ's' is neuter. In particular, if we are to preserve these rules, 'Something ϕ's' will be neuter when all singular ϕx's are neuter, as in the case we are now considering. We can work this out from the table for Łukasiewicz's 3-valued implication, which is as follows (using 1 for 'true', 2 for 'neuter', and 3 for 'false'):

C	1	2	3
*1	1	2	3
2	1	1	2
3	1	1	1

Consider first the rule that we may infer 'If something ϕ's then β' from 'If x ϕ's then β', given that the latter expresses a logical law and that x does not occur freely in β, that is, that the truth-value of β can vary independently of that of ϕx. It is given that $C\phi x\beta$ expresses a law, that is, has the value 1 for all values of ϕx and β, and we are considering a ϕ such that ϕx always has the value 2. $C2\beta = 1$ so long as β has the value 1 or 2, so β can have either of these values. If it has the value 1, $C\Sigma x\phi x\beta$ will be a law no matter what the value of $\Sigma x\phi x$; but if β has the value 2, $C\Sigma x\phi x\beta$ will be a law only if $\Sigma x\phi x$ has the value 2 or 3; and since β can have the value 2, $\Sigma x\phi x$ must have the value 2 or 3 to preserve this rule. Consider now the other rule, that given a law of the form $C\alpha\phi x$ we can infer $C\alpha\Sigma x\phi x$ as a law. When $\phi x = 2$, $C\alpha\phi x$ will be a law so long as α has the value 2 or 3; but if α can take the value 2, $C\alpha\Sigma x\phi x$ will only be a law if $\Sigma x\phi x$ has the value 2 or 1. So to preserve one rule, $\Sigma x\phi x$ must under these circumstances have the value 2 or 3; to preserve the other, it must under these circumstances have the value 2 or 1; and we can only preserve both if under these circumstances $\Sigma x\phi x$ has the value 2. (The values for $\Sigma x\phi x$ under the other circumstances mentioned are worked out in a similar way.) And, to return to our people on the cliff, if 'x will fall over' is undecided and so neuter in truth-value, for each individual x, then the statement 'There is someone who will fall over' is also neuter in truth-value. If, at the same time, the statement 'It will be the case that someone falls over' is true, the implication 'If it will be the case that someone falls over then there is someone of whom it will be the case that he falls over', will have the truth-value $C12$, that is (by Łukasiewicz's table for C), 2.

Where p is a statement in the past tense, it would seem that p and Lp are equivalent without qualification. That was in effect the first premiss of the Master Argument, and we saw, and see, no reason for calling it in question. For with the past, there can be no question of alternative possibilities being open, except in some purely subjective or relative sense of 'possibility'. It is possible that Caesar had mumps as a child, and possible that he did not, only in the sense that we do not know that he did not or that he did, or in the sense that nothing now known entails one thing or the other; but the fact is that either he definitely did have them or he definitely did not. In other words, if 'It has been the case that p' is not definitely true, it is definitely false; there are no neuter statements in the past tense—with what is past, openness to alternatives has gone. For example, considering our people on the cliff again, if the statement 'It will be the case that x falls over' is neither true nor false, then the statement 'It has been the case that it will be the case that x falls over' is definitely false; this simply *has not* yet been the case, though it may come to be the case later, if and when the possibility of not falling over ceases to be open to x. Hence if we confine its application to statements in the past tense, or indeed to any class of statements which are already definitely true or false, this 3-valued logic can be collapsed into the ordinary 2-valued, just as the system Q can be collapsed into S5 if we confine its application to statements containing no logical proper names.

I do not propose to consider at all fully the modifications of tense-logic which the admission of a third truth-value, interpreted as above, would entail; but one or two details are worth mentioning. Suppose we gear our tense-logic to something like Leśniewski's ontology, so that we do not need to worry about statements becoming or having been unformulable or truth-valueless, and lay down postulates for a 'logic of futurity' and an analogous 'logic of pastness', to be subjoined to the 3-valued C–N calculus. So far as I can see there is no reason why we should not retain the postulates laid down for the logic of futurity in Lecture II, i.e. the rule RF $(a{\rightarrow}Fn\alpha)$ and the axioms $CFnNpNFnp$, $CNFnpFnNp$, $CFopp$, etc. And we may lay down past-tense analogues for most of these; but not for

CNFnpFnNp. That is, we cannot have as an axiom *CNPnpPnNp*, 'If it was not the case *n* days ago that *p* then it was the case *n* days ago that not *p*'; for *n* days ago the statement *p* might have been (though formulable) neither true nor false, in which case both the statements 'It was the case *n* days ago that *p*' and 'It was the case *n* days ago that not *p*' would be false, and the implication *CNPnpPnNp* would have a true antecedent and a false consequent. *CPnNpNPnp*, *CPopp*, and the analogues of the other axioms of futurity seem all right, but one consequence of the rejection of *CNPnpPnNp* is this: In the logic of futurity we can prove the converse of the axiom *CFopp* as follows:

1. *CFopp* 2. *CNFnpFnNp*
3. *CCpNqCqNp* 4. *CCNpqCNqp*
5. *CCpqCCqrCpr*
   3 *p/FoNp, q/p = C1 p/Np—6*
6. *CpNFoNp*
   4 *p/Fop, q/FoNp = C2 n/o—7*
7. *CNFoNpFop*
   5 *q/NFoNp, r/Fop = C6—C7—8*
8. *CpFop*.

And as formulae 3–5 hold in 3-valued as well as 2-valued propositional logic, this proof is still available to us. But we cannot analogously prove *CpPop*, since we have not the analogue of formula 2; and the rejection of *CpPop* is intuitively justifiable, for if *p* is neuter in truth-value, what it asserts *has not yet* come to pass, and *Pop*, which would assert that it *has just*—right now— come to pass, is not merely neuter but false. And this leads to yet another asymmetry. One proof which is possible in the logic of futurity, since we have *CpFop*, is the following:

1. *CpFop* 2. *Cpp*
3. *CCpqCCqrCpr*
   2 *p/Fnp × Σ2n = 4*
4. *CFnpΣnFnp*
   3 *p/ΠnPnp, q/FoΠnPnp, r/ΣnFnΠnPnp*
    = *C1 p/ΠnPnp—C4 n/o, p/ΠnPnp—5*
5. *CΠnPnpΣnFnΠnPnp*.

That is, if it always has been the case that p, then it (is or) will be the case that it always has been the case that p. But the analogue of this, i.e. the formula $C\Pi nFnp\Sigma nPn\Pi nFnp$, 'If it (is and) always will be the case that p, then it has been the case that it (is and) always will be the case that p',[1] is not provable— and ought not to be, since if its antecedent is neuter its consequent is false. The substitution p/Np in this last formula gives us something which means 'If it (is not and) never will be the case that p, then it has been the case that it (is not and) never will be the case that p', which is the proposition I take to be mistakenly assumed as a law in the Diodoran 'Master-Argument'.

The construction of a characteristic matrix for this type of logic presents serious difficulties. It is certainly not possible to arrive at one by an intuitive procedure analogous to that used in obtaining our infinite matrix for Q. For suppose we begin, as before, with an artificially simplified universe in which there are only the two times today and yesterday, the possible 'values' of p being 'true both times', 'true today but neuter yesterday', 'true today but false yesterday', 'neuter today but true yesterday', and so on (there will be nine in all). And suppose p to be true today, though it was false yesterday; what, in that case, will have been the value yesterday of 'It will be the case that p'? Our data do not give the question a determinate answer—if p is true today, 'It will be the case that p' might have been true yesterday, but might equally well have been neuter. Hence Fp is not a truth-function of p even in our extended sense of 'truth-function', for its 'value' (sequence of ordinary truth-values) is not unambiguously determined by the 'value' of its argument. This logic is therefore not capable of being represented as a many-valued truth-functional system, in this sense of 'truth-functional'; though there may well be some other extension of the notion of a 'truth-function' which would make such a representation possible.

Another complication which arises in this type of tense-logic is the following: In the logic of futurity developed in Lecture II

---

[1] In this verbalization I write '(is and) always will be' for ΠnFn, and in the preceding case '(is or) will be' for ΣnFn because Fop is equivalent to p, but I do not represent ΠnPn and ΣnPn in this way, as Pop is not equivalent to p, but only implies it.

we found it reasonable to define the simple 'It will be the case that p' as an abbreviation for 'For some n, it will be the case after the interval n that p'. But this definition is no longer quite satisfactory; for it may be quite definite that it will be the case that p, even though there is no time of which it can be definitely said that it will *then* be the case that p. That is, none of our Fnp's will have the value 1, so that $\Sigma nFnp$ will not have the value 1, and yet the plain Fp *will* have the value 1. And to find an alternative definition is a little puzzling; for even when we distinguish $F\Sigma x\phi x$ and $\Sigma xF\phi x$ as in the last lecture, we cannot make the same sort of distinction with the quantifier (binding times) which would be a part of F itself, if F were definable in this way. We can, however, solve this problem if we may assume (and the assumption seems reasonable) that 'It will be the case that p' is definitely true only if the time at which p will be the case is not quite indefinitely far away; that is, only if, for some sufficiently large n, it (definitely) will be the case n time-units hence that p has been the case. We could then define Fp as $\Sigma nFn\Sigma mPmp$. Alternatively we could define Fp, as before, as $\Sigma nFnp$, read the preceding as 'It *will have been* the case that p', and make our present point by saying that 'It will have been the case that p' does not always entail 'It will be the case that p' (since the former may have the value 1 when the latter has the value 2, and $C12 = 2$).

Nor, it may be noted, does 'It will be the case that p' (in the sense of $\Sigma nFnp$) imply 'It will have been the case that p'. For there are some formulae, e.g. $KpNp$, whose exemplifications are never true, though they are not always false. For example, in 'There will be a sea-battle tomorrow and there will not be a sea-battle tomorrow', both conjuncts might at some times be neuter and therefore the whole conjunction neuter; though at no time will this proposition be true. So long as there are such times, $\Sigma nFnp$ will have for this p the value 2. But 'It has been the case that there will and will not, etc.', will be definitely false until the argument is definitely true, i.e. it will be definitely false always; and so 'It will have been the case that, etc.', is at all times definitely false. Hence in a case of this sort $CFpFPp = C23 = 2$. On the other hand, if $F\alpha$ is a theorem, and so definitely true for all values of its variables, $FP\alpha$ will also be a theorem.

X

Indeterminism without Neuter Propositions

USING 'truth-value' in the sense of 'momentary truth-value', is it really necessary to admit three truth-values in order to bring out the logical asymmetry between past and future which a serious indeterminism seems to demand? So far as I can see, it is not. Three-valued logic is only one way of handling this problem. I can think of at least two others, and one of these I wish, in the end, seriously to recommend to you.

How we deal with this sort of thing in ordinary speech has been very well described by Professor Ryle in his Tarner Lectures. We operate, to put it briefly, with a notion of 'retrospective verification'. That is, we use the phrase 'was true' more or less as follows: Suppose that on Tuesday someone says 'There will be a sea-battle tomorrow', and on Wednesday the sea-battle turns up. We may then say, on Wednesday, 'You were right yesterday about the sea-battle', or 'Your prediction has been verified', or 'What you said was true'. But this 'was true' is not a genuine past tense but a makeshift. All that is meant is that the person *said* there would be a sea-battle, and now there *is* one, and if this conjunction of a past-tense statement with a present-tense one is to be contracted into one with a single main verb it does not much matter whether that verb be in the present tense or in the past. But ' "There will be a sea-battle tomorrow" *is* true', said on Wednesday, suggests a sea-battle on *Thursday*; so the form chosen is 'was true', though this also could mislead, and does mislead—by suggesting that there was on Tuesday some fact (the fact that there *was going to be* a sea-battle) with which the statement then accorded. This suggestion, however, is not really intended[1]—in this sense of 'was true', 'The statement "There will be a sea-battle" *was* true' does not entail 'The statement "There was going to be a sea-battle" *is* true'.

It would be pointless to deny the permissibility and intelligibility of the common use of 'was true'; and I am not primarily concerned to discuss statements and their truth-values at all.

---

[1] Ryle, *Dilemmas*, pp. 19-20.

What I primarily wish to formalize—and I wish to formalize this partly because I myself believe in it—is the view that from the *fact* that there is a sea-battle going on it does not follow that there *was going to be* one, though it does follow that there *will have been* one. Once this much is admitted, the problem of how to describe Tuesday's prediction of Wednesday's sea-battle can be settled in different ways. We can say, if we like, that there was nothing at all to be said on Tuesday about its truth-value, but that on Wednesday 'It was true' would be the proper verdict; or we can say that 'It is neuter' would have been the proper description of it on Tuesday and 'It was neuter' the proper one on Wednesday. The former way of talking is closer to ordinary speech as it now is, but the latter gives us a tidier semantics—tidier in two ways: (a) it preserves, or seems to preserve, the rule that '*p was* true' entails ' "It was the case that *p*" *is* true', and (b) it ensures that *p* has *some* truth-value or other at all times. But both these advantages can be secured in other ways.

The third solution I want to propose arises immediately out of the comparison with 'intentional' logic with which we began. The fact that *x* may neither think that *p* nor think that not *p* can certainly be expressed without employing a neuter truth-value. In such a case we may simply say that '*x* thinks that *p*' and '*x* thinks that not *p*' are both plain false and '*x* does not think that *p*' and '*x* does not think that not *p*' both plain true. The law of excluded middle makes it necessary to say that either *x* thinks that *p* or *x* does not think that *p*, and that either *x* thinks that not *p* or *x* does not think that not *p*, but it does not make it necessary to say that either *x* thinks that *p* or *x* thinks that not *p*. And perhaps the undetermined future can be similarly handled—where the question as to whether *p* will eventuate or not is undecided, we might say that both 'It will be the case that *p*' and 'It will be the case that not *p*' are plain false, while 'It will not be the case that *p*' (i.e. 'It is not the case that it will be the case that *p*') and 'It will not be the case that not *p*' are both plain true; and that the law of excluded middle guarantees that either it will be the case that *p* or it will not be the case that *p*, and that either it will be the case that not *p* or it will not be the case that not *p*, and perhaps even that it will be the case that either *p* or not *p*, but not that either it will be the case that *p* or it will be the case that not p. This way of talking departs from ordinary idiom, so far as I can see, at one point only. To say 'It will not be the case that p' when the futurition of p is undetermined seems a little strong; but this is only because in ordinary speech 'It will not be the case that p' tends to be used indifferently for

'It is not the case that it will be the case that p'

and

'It will be the case that it is not the case that p',

and it *would* be wrong to say the latter when the futurition of p is undetermined. There is to some extent the same ambiguity about 'does not think'. 'x does not think that p' might mean 'It is not the case that x thinks that p', but it might also mean 'x thinks that not p'.

In a system expressing the point of view just sketched, $CNFnpFnNp$ will not hold, but $CNFnpPnNp$ will. $CNFnpFnNp$ will not hold because when it is undecided whether it will be p or not-p which eventuates n time-units hence, 'It is not the case that p will be the case', $NFnp$, is true, while 'It will be that p is not the case', $FnNp$, is false. But 'It was not the case that p' does entail 'It was the case that not p', for even if it was undetermined n days ago that p—which has now occurred—would occur n days later, this does not mean that

(i) 'It was not the case n days ago that p would be the case n days later' ($NPnFnp$)

is true and

(ii) 'It was the case n days ago that it was not the case that p would be the case n days later' ($PnNFnp$)

is false. For (ii) is true too, on our present ruling.[1] On the supposition we are making, n days ago Fnp and $FnNp$ were both false, and $NFnp$ and $NFnNp$ therefore both true, so that $PnNFnp$ is now true as well as $NPnFnp$.

We cannot in this system introduce modal operators which are *quite* like the 3-valued M and L. But a quasi-modal operator

---

[1] This means that with this system the answer to Diodorus is that p does not entail that it has not been the case that it will not be the case that p—we reject $CpNPNFp$.

$M(f)n$, to be read as 'It will possibly be the case n days hence that . . .', can be defined as $NFnN$, 'It is not the case that it will be the case n days hence that not . . .'. $M(f)np$ as thus defined will be true if either it will be the case n days hence that p, or the point is undetermined. We will thus have $CFnpM(f)np$ as a law but not its converse $CM(f)npFnp$, nor will the plain $M(f)np$ be a law. But the corresponding L, with $L(f)n$ defined as $NM(f)nN$, will not be 'modal' even to this extent, being equivalent to Fn. For $NM(f)nN = NNFnNN = Fn$. That is, 'It will be the case that p' is true if and only if 'It will necessarily be the case that p' is true.

But at this point our system, though not quite like 3-valued logic, is more like it than you might think. A rather curious feature of 3-valued logic which has not been sufficiently noticed is that although its forms Lp ('Definitely p') and Mp ('p is still open') are both in one sense modal forms, as 'modal' is defined by Łukasiewicz, in another sense not more than one of them can be—in this other sense a 3-valued logic only allows of a *semi-*modal system. They are both modal forms in the sense that all eight of Łukasiewicz's criteria are met if we define C, N, M, and L by the usual tables, namely

C	1	2	3	N	M	L
*1	1	2	3	3	1	1
2	1	1	2	2	1	3
3	1	1	1	1	3	3

But while these tables all have a certain naturalness, it is well known that they do not verify all the laws of the ordinary propositional calculus. For example, they do not verify the *consequentia mirabilis* $CCNppp$, 'What is implied by its own negation is true'. The very virtues of the systems are bound up with this fact—for example, the quite remarkable fact that the modal operators are definable in terms of this C and N—Mp as $CNpp$ and Lp in the ordinary way as $NMNp$, i.e. $NCNNpNp$. This definition of M turns the formula $CCNppp$ into $CMpp$, and there is something intuitively very pleasing about this. This is a formula which when added to the axioms of the system makes it 2-valued (the definition of Apq as $CCpqq$ turns the same formula $CCNppp$ into the law of excluded middle $ANpp$); and if we interpret the process of turning 3-valued logic into 2-valued as a declaration that our propositional variables are now to be taken as standing only for statements about what has already come to pass, it is fitting that this restriction should be enshrined in a formula which can be read as equating the possible and the real. For with regard to what has already come to pass, only the real *is* possible—God Himself, as Agathon says, cannot now make that different. So the non-classical character of this C and N seems to me no substantial objection to describing this system as modal. Nevertheless, if the C and N occurring in the formulae $CLpp$, $CpLp$, and NLp are taken to be operators for which all the classical laws for 'if' and 'not' do hold, it is doubtful whether Łukasiewicz's conditions for L and M can be met in a 3-valued system.

It is certainly possible in such a system to construct a C and N for which all the ordinary laws hold. As I have shown elsewhere,[1] they hold for any 3-valued C and N with tables of the following form, where $\bar{1}$ stands for either value other than 1:

C	1	$\bar{1}$	N
*1	1	$\bar{1}$	$\bar{1}$
$\bar{1}$	1	1	1

For example, Słupecki's 1946 C and N with the tables

C	1	2	3	N
*1	1	2	3	3
2	1	1	1	1
3	1	1	1	1

And with tables of this type for C and N Łukasiewicz's conditions for M (that $CpMp$ is a law but not Mp or $CMpp$) will be met by any operator with a table of either of the following types:

p	Mp	Mp
*1	1	1
2	$\bar{1}$	1
3	1	$\bar{1}$

But with tables of this sort for C and N, there can be no operator

[1] *Formal Logic*, pp. 239-40.

meeting Łukasiewicz's conditions for L. For (a) if $CLpp$ is to be a law, Lp must not be 1 when p is not 1, since $C1\bar{1} = \bar{1}$; but (b) if $CpLp$ is *not* to be a law, Lp must not be 1 when p *is* 1, for $C11 = 1$ (and $CpLp$ cannot be refuted when p is not 1, since $C\bar{1}\alpha = 1$ for any α). Hence Lp cannot ever take the value 1; but in that case (c) NLp will be a law, since $N\bar{1} = 1$, so that Łukasiewicz's third condition will not be met.

The preceding way of defining a 3-valued C and N for which all the classical laws will hold is the one which would be adopted by someone holding that truth and falsity are the only truth-values, that the numbers 2 and 3 merely designate different kinds of false propositions, and that functions whose truth-values may differ according to whether their arguments have the value 2 or 3 are not truth-functions.[1] Another way, which would be favoured by someone who regarded 1 and 2 as merely designating different kinds of truths, would be to have two designated values (1 and 2) and tables of the form

C	$\bar{3}$	3	N
*$\bar{3}$	$\bar{3}$	3	3
3	$\bar{3}$	$\bar{3}$	$\bar{3}$

e.g. the tables[2]

C	1	2	3	N
*1	1	2	3	3
*2	1	1	3	3
3	1	2	1	1

With tables like this for C and N it is possible to meet Łukasiewicz's conditions for L by using either of the following two tables:

p	Lp	Lp
*1	$\bar{3}$	3
*2	3	$\bar{3}$
3	3	3

---

[1] For a further description of one point of view of this type, see my note on 'Curry's Paradox and Three-valued Logic', *Australasian Journal of Philosophy*, Dec. 1955.

[2] This C is the C_1 of p. 51 of B. Sobociński's 'Axiomatization of a Partial System of Three-value Calculus of Propositions', *Journal of Computing Systems*, vol. i, No. 1 (1952), Paper 3. The N is definable in terms of this C and Sobociński's other undefined operator H as $CpHCpp$ ($Hp = (3, 1, 2)p$).

but there is no way of meeting his conditions for M. For (i) to have $CpMp$ a law, Mp must not be 3 when p is not 3 (for then $C\bar{3}M\bar{3} = C\bar{3}3 = 3$); but (ii) to reject $CMpp$, Mp must not be 3 when p is 3 (for $CMpp$ can only take the value 3 when p has the value 3 and Mp some other value), but (iii) if Mp never takes the value 3 at all, it will be a law, contrary to Łukasiewicz's third condition.

We can return now to my alternative system. What we have here is in effect a quasi-3-valued system, in which (*a*) C and N obey all the classical laws, and (*b*) the form Fnp, and one derivative form (namely, $FnNp$) are capable of having two sorts of falsehood. That is, '$Fnp = 2$' and '$Fnp = 3$' both mean 'Fnp is false', but '$Fnp = 2$' means 'Fnp is false because the futurition of p is as yet undetermined' and '$Fnp = 3$' means 'Fnp is false because $FnNp$ is true', so that we have these tables:

Fnp	FnNp	NFnp	M(f)np	M(f)nNp	NM(f)np	NM(f)nNp	KM(f)npM(f)nNP
1	3	3	1	3	3	1	3
2	2	1	1	1	3	3	1
3	1	1	3	1	1	3	3

These tables are like those for p, Np, Mp, MNp, etc., in Łukasiewicz's 3-valued system, but (i) because the two truth-operators must be supposed to have a table of the form

C	1	$\bar{1}$	N
1	1	$\bar{1}$	$\bar{1}$
$\bar{1}$	1	1	1

we have a theorem like $CpLp$ (strictly, $CFnpNM(f)nNp$), and (ii) only with Fnp and its derivative has the distinction between the values 3 and 2 any significance.[1] We could, indeed, define an operator $M(p)n$, 'It has possibly been the case n days ago that . . .', as $NPnN$, but this 'possibility', as well as the corresponding 'Necessity', will be equivalent to plain truth, since $NPnN = PnNN = Pn$.

If we introduce 'modal' operators into this tense-logic in the other way, i.e. if we use Mp for 'p at some time' and Lp for 'p at all times', even the modal logic we obtain for use without logical

---

[1] For other combinations of 2-valued truth-functions with 3-valued functions of another sort, see my review of Kalinowski's paper on 'Normative Logic' in the *Journal of Symbolic Logic*, June 1956, pp. 191–2.

proper names will be more complicated than S5. In particular, we will not be able to equate Mp with $NLNp$, or Lp with $NMNp$, nor will we have such allied equations as that of MNp with NLp and of NMp with LNp. For example, let p be 'There is a battle on the moon', and let it be supposed that there neither is nor has yet been a battle on the moon, that with the nearer future times it is certain that there will not be one then, and with the remoter ones it is uncertain whether there will be, i.e. with these remaining t's we have both 'Not p-at-t' and 'Not not-p-at-t'. There is thus no t such that p at t, i.e. we have NMp; but it is not the case that for all t we have not-p at t, i.e. we have not LNp. At this point our indeterminist tense-logic resembles the system Q, but it is not quite identical with Q all the same. For example, there seems no reason to drop the rule that if α expresses a law so does $L\alpha$, or the rule underlying this, that if α expresses a law so does $Ut\alpha$. Even if α is, say, 'Either there is or there is not a battle on the moon', exemplifying the law of excluded middle $ApNp$, and t is a time for which we have as yet neither Utp nor $UtNp$ with 'There is a battle on the moon' for our p—even then, there is no reason why we should not have $UtApNp$, 'Either-p-or-not-p at t'.

As with the tense-logic which allows for a neuter (momentary) truth value, it is difficult to construct, on an intuitive basis, a characteristic matrix for this system. Using our sequences of 1's and 3's for truth-values, where the sequence for p has a 1 at the point that means now, the sequence for Fnp might have either a 1 or 3 at the point that means the time n units before now (a 1 if p's present truth was then determined, a 3 if it was not). There are also, as in the 3-valued system, grounds for denying that 'It will have been the case that p' entails 'It will be the case that p', when the latter is taken to mean 'For some n, it will be the case that n time-units hence that p'; though there are no longer grounds for denying the converse implication.

We might describe a system in which a tense-logic of the type now sketched is associated with ϵ-functions as $\Sigma T4$. Some intriguing problems arise in connexion with the verification of the form ϵab in such a system, even when something like the strong 'the' of $\Sigma T3$ is used. So long as it is undetermined whether there will be a unique a, statements of the form $F\epsilon ab$ and of course ϵab will be false. But let us revert to our people on the cliff, and consider the term 'person who is, has been, or will be the first to fall over' (on the occasion in question). It is, *ex hypothesi*, already determined that there will be such a person, so for this *a* there are already true statements of the form $F\epsilon ab$. But are there yet, for this *a*, any true statements of the form ϵab? For example, is it already true that the first-one-to-fall is among the people now on the cliff? It seems to me that at this point we are again faced with a strong and a weak sense of 'the'. In the strong sense which we might symbolize as $\epsilon_{,}$, there are as yet no true statements about *the* first-one-to-fall, for there is as yet no one of whom it is true that *he* (is, has been, or) will be the first one to fall. But in another sense, the first-to-fall is already one of those on the cliff. And a possible definition of the weak 'the' (call it ϵ', for it is still 'strong' in the sense of $\Sigma T3$) in terms of the strong $\epsilon_{,}$ is suggested by the following consideration: Suppose that in the end it is a certain Mr. Adams who falls first. Once he has achieved this distinction, or once it has become a definite fact that he will do so, it is possible to make true statements of the form 'The first faller is ($\epsilon_{,}$) a so-and-so', and among these true statements will be 'The first faller is one-who-was-among-the-people-on-the-cliff'. And this suggests that 'the first faller is (weaker ϵ) a so-and-so' may be defined as

'For some *n*, it will be the case *n* time-units hence that the first faller is one who was a so-and-so *n* time-units ago'.

Symbolically, we may build up this definition as follows: Let the term-symbol $\lambda\phi$ mean '*x* such that ϕx', and let us express $\epsilon_{,}ab$ as a monadic function of *a* by writing it as $(\epsilon_{,}b)a$. Then $\lambda(\epsilon_{,}b)$ will be the term 'thing that is a *b*', and $\lambda Pn(\epsilon_{,}b)$ will be the term 'thing that was a *b* *n* time-units ago'. Our definition of the weaker ϵ (call it ϵ') then becomes

$$\epsilon'ab = \Sigma nFn\epsilon_{,}a\lambda Pn(\epsilon_{,}b).$$

Not, be it noted, $\epsilon'ab = \Sigma nFnPn\epsilon_{,}ab,$

'For some *n*, it will be the case *n* days hence that it was the case *n* days back that the *a* is ($\epsilon_{,}$) a *b*'. For while, once the identity of the first faller is fixed, we can truly describe the first faller as one-who-was-on-the-cliff, we still cannot say that it was the case that the first faller is ($\epsilon_{,}$) on the cliff.

Another oddity in $\Sigma T4$ is this: Suppose that in $\Sigma T3$ we use the form $I''ab$ for 'The a and the b are one', in a sense in which it could be true although the a and the b do not now exist. That is, we take $I''ab$ to mean 'It is, has been, or will be the case that the a is the b', $MI'ab$. Let us, further, use the form $II''ab$ for 'The a and the b are two', again in a sense in which it could be true even if the a and the b do not now exist. We can define $II''ab$ in this sense as

'The a is-an-identifiable-individual, and so is the b, and it is always the case that the a is not identical with the b',

$KK\epsilon''ai\epsilon''biLNI'ab$ (where $\epsilon''ai = Mob'a$). We then have, as a law of $\Sigma T3$, the formula

$$CK\epsilon''ai\epsilon''biAI''abII''ab,$$

'If the a is-an-identifiable-individual and so is the b, then either the a and the b are one or the a and the b are two'. But in $\Sigma T4$ this law, with ϵ'' replaced by $\epsilon_{,,}$, I'' by $I_{,,}$, with II'' by $II_{,,}$ ($\epsilon_{,,}$, $I_{,,}$, and $II_{,,}$ being defined in terms of ϵ, in the same way as the others are defined in terms of ϵ'), does not hold. For, taking our example of the people on the cliff, Mr. Adams is an identifiable individual and the first faller is an identifiable individual (in the sense that it either is, has been, or will be the case that the first faller exists), but it is not the case that Mr. Adams and the first faller are one, nor is it the case that Mr. Adams and the first faller are two. It neither is, has been, nor (yet) will be the case that Mr. Adams is the first faller, so they are not one; and it is not (yet) the case that it will be the case that Mr. Adams is not the first faller, so they are not two either. The $\Sigma T3$ law will of course still hold for objects which have already come into existence (in a sense in which the first faller has not yet done so), even if they have now ceased to exist, so we have now a clear sense in which past objects have a definite identity which future objects may lack. With a's like our 'first faller' it is in fact inaccurate to read $\epsilon''ai$ as 'The a is-an-*identifiable*-individual'.

APPENDIX A

Tenses and Truth in the History of Logic

AMONG ancient and medieval logicians it was taken for granted that (i) tense-distinctions are a proper subject of logical reflection, and that (ii) what is true at one time is in many cases false at another time, and vice versa. I do not propose to document this statement, but the tense-logic of the ancients and especially of the Schoolmen is certainly something about which a book ought to be written, and I hope that the present attempt at an independent development of the subject will be of use to whoever, in the end, does write it.

After the Renaissance both (i) and (ii)—first (i) and then (ii)—came to be more and more widely denied. As to (i), I have the impression that logicians first dropped the study of tense-distinct-tions, as they dropped the study of modality and of the theory of *consequentiae*, because they had ceased to be interested in them, and later found arguments to justify this neglect. Arguments tending that way, however, were forthcoming quite early. For example, in the *Port-Royal Logic* there is a passage (lifted from the *General Grammar* of the same authors) attacking Aristotle's view that it is essential to a verb to have some reference to time. The only quite universal function of a verb (in the indicative) is said to be that of expressing affirmation. Only the simple 'is', and not always that, is a pure verb by this criterion. The same word which expresses affirmation may also indicate what is affirmed (as 'lives', for example, indicates not only that we are affirming something of the subject but that that something is living), and it may indicate a time; but these features of some verbs are as little part of their verbal character as the indications of the *subject* which they contain in some inflected languages. There are verbs which have no time reference (as the 'is' in 'God is infinite' or 'The whole is greater than its parts'), and a time-reference may be conveyed by parts of speech, e.g. participles, which are not verbs.[1]

There is no echo here, it should be noted, of the scientific locution 'at time *t*', though the new physics might well have been expected to be responsible for the casual attitude to tenses in post-Renaissance logicians. Possibly it was, in an indirect way—these new interests may help to explain *why* they were no longer interested in tenses. But what is explicit here is not this at all, but the view that the

[1] *Port-Royal Logic*, Part II, ch. ii.

copula, considered as the main *formal* element in a proposition, simply expresses the putting together by the mind of certain 'ideas'. And so it was to be for some time to come, and especially in the nineteenth century, when it was a very popular view among logicians that in putting a statement into strict 'logical form' any time-indication which its verb may contain should go not into the copula but into the terms. According to Whately,

> The Copula, as such, has no relation to *time*, but expresses merely the agreement or disagreement of two given terms: hence, if any other *tense* of the substantive-verb besides the present, is used, . . . if the circumstance of *time* do really *modify the sense* of the whole proposition, . . . then this circumstance is to be regarded as part of one of the terms: . . . as 'this man *was* honest'; i.e. 'he is one formerly-honest'.[1]

The Hamiltonians were particularly emphatic on this point, and their reason for it particularly explicit. Says Mansel,

> The office of the verb in Logic is not to declare the past or future connection of an attribute with its subject in the represented fact, but to declare the present coexistence of two concepts in the representative act of thought.[2]

And Bowen,

> The Copula of a Judgment, since it expresses the *present* union of two thoughts now before the mind, must always appear as the *present tense* of a verb. . . . Thus the Propositions . . . *he came yesterday: John will arrive*, if reduced to their logical form as Judgments, must be thus expressed . . . *he is the person who came yesterday; John is he who will arrive.*[3]

And Fowler,

> It is simply the office of the proposition to express my present judgment as to the agreement or disagreement of two terms. Hence all reference to time, past or future, and even to time present, as respects the terms themselves, and not my judgment as to their agreement, must be expressed in the predicate and not in the copula. I may, for brevity's sake, say . . . 'Alexander was the son of Philip', 'The guns will be fired tomorrow' . . . but formally, for the purpose of being estimated logically, I must resolve them into their logical elements, and say . . . 'Alexander *is* a person who was son of Philip', 'The firing of the guns *is* an event which will take place tomorrow'.[4]

One notices a certain movement here from the view that the tense of the copula must always be the present, to the view that it

---

[1] R. Whately, *Elements of Logic*, II. i. 2.
[2] H. L. Mansel, *Prolegomena Logica*, 2nd ed. (1860), p. 72.
[3] Francis Bowen, *A Treatise on Logic* (1870), pp. 107–8.
[4] Thomas Fowler, *Deductive Logic*, 10th ed. (1895), p. 26.

has no tense at all. Fowler professes to be of the latter party; but he makes no serious attempt to fit his examples to his theory. (What place can a word like 'tomorrow' have in a strictly tenseless form?) And there is a strong tendency to make this 'putting into the predicate' little more than a crude reproduction of the original statement as a subordinate clause. This way we can undoubtedly put any statement at all into the present tense, since any p whatever can be inflated to 'That p, is the case' (cf. our Lecture II, on the superfluity of a special present-tense-operator). But not only tense but even quantity and quality can be dealt with thus; 'No men are mortal' too is equivalent to 'That no men are mortal is the case', or 'The case is that no men are mortal'. In other words, any statement whatever can be put not only into the present tense but also into the form of a singular affirmative. If we did try this on with 'No men are mortal', any logical traditionalist, even a Hamiltonian, would be quick enough to point out that now everything of logical interest had gone into the terms; but can we not say the same of tenses, and say it even when the method of 'reduction' is not as crude as this? Even if tense-distinctions *can* all be thrown into the terms, it does not follow automatically that they are of no logical interest; for terms too may have a 'logical form'. There is a logic, for example, of conjunctive and alternative terms ('Every X is Y or Z' entails 'Every X that is not Y is Z', and so on), so why not one of terms like Whately's 'formerly-honest'? Nor is there the least perception of the problems to which a programme of this sort, when seriously carried out, gives rise. 'He is one formerly-honest' and 'He is the person who came yesterday' are Whately's and Bowen's renderings of 'This man was honest' and 'He came yesterday', but what if since then he has ceased to exist? (Fowler, since he takes the tenseless line, can doubtless say that the Alexander of 'Alexander is a person who was the son of Philip' exists a-temporally.)

In the midst of this chorus—a dreadful one, by Quine-Smart standards as well as my own—there was one good resonant voice of dissent, that of John Stuart Mill. Mill, significantly, appends what he has to say on this point to a discussion of Hobbes's theory that even negation ought properly to be thought of as a qualification of the predicate rather than of the copula. He says of this that

> To put things together, and to put or keep them asunder, will remain different operations, whatever tricks we play with language,

and goes on,

> A remark of a similar nature may be applied to most of those distinctions among propositions which are said to have reference to their *modality*; as

difference of time or tense; the sun *did* rise, the sun *is* rising, the sun *will* rise. These differences, like that between affirmation and negation, might be glossed over by considering the incident of time as a mere modification of the predicate: thus, *The sun is an object having risen,* The sun is *an object now rising,* The sun is *an object to rise hereafter.* But the simplification would be merely verbal. Past, present and future do not constitute so many different kinds of rising; they are designations belonging to the event asserted, to the *sun's* rising today. They affect, not the predicate, but the applicability of the predicate to the particular subject. That which we affirm to be past, present or future, is not what the subject signifies, nor what the predicate signifies, but specifically and expressly what the predication signifies; what is expressed only by the proposition as such, and not by either or both of the terms. Therefore the circumstance of time is properly considered as attaching to the copula, which is the sign of predication, not to the predicate.[1]

Mill said that; but unhappily that is *all* that he said. He made no attempt to work out what it would mean in detail to treat distinctions of tense as seriously as the distinction between affirmation and denial; though his one small cry in the wilderness makes it seem a happy chance that the 1949 *Utp* logic of Łoś was developed as part of an attempted formalization of Mill's canons of induction. (Even Łoś's logic is not, indeed, a tense-logic but rather an unanalysed date-and-interval logic, but it is at least a logic in which the time-reference is made by an operator which takes whole 'predications' as its arguments.)

In view of his failure to develop it further, it is hardly surprising that Mill's protest found no echoes, and the Hamiltonian viewpoint continued to dominate the nineteenth-century logical scene. Thus we find Minto, at the end of the century, writing as follows:

> Seeing that the Copula in S is P . . . does not express time, but only a certain relation between S and P, the question arises Where are we to put time in the analytic formula? . . . The common technical treatment is to view the tense as part of the predicate. 'All had fled', i.e. the whole subject is included in a class constituted on the attributes of flight at a given time. It may be that the Predicate is solely a predicate of time. 'The Board met yesterday at noon.' S is P, i.e. the meeting of the Board is one of the events characterised by having happened at a certain time. . . . But in some cases the time is more properly regarded as part of the subject, e.g. 'Wheat is dear'. S does not stand here for wheat collectively, but for the wheat now in the market, the wheat of the present time.[2]

There are some differences in emphasis here, however, from what

---

[1] J. S. Mill, *System of Logic,* i. iv. 2.
[2] W. Minto, *Logic Inductive & Deductive,* 1915 reprint, pp. 77–78.

we have had till now, and I do not mean merely that Minto sees the subject as well as· the predicate as a possible vehicle of time-references. This is a respectable piece of logical writing, by comparison with Mansel, Bowen, and Fowler, and among other things their 'Conceptualism' has gone. What is logically important is not now the mind's present putting together of ideas, but the objective relation of one class of objects or events to another. And the tense-less rather than the present-tense character of the copula is more consistently maintained than in Fowler (though the Board's meeting is still said to be 'characterised by *having happened . . .*') We have something now that begins to sound like the 'time *t*' of the scientists, and a basis for denying the assumption of the ancients and the Schoolmen that what is true now may in some cases be false here-after. Of writers making this point in a traditional context, the most explicit is Keynes, who says in the last edition of his *Formal Logic*,

> Some judgments . . . contain an explicit or implicit reference to time. But this is really part of the judgment. As soon as the judgment is fully stated it becomes independent of time. It may perhaps be said that the judgment *France is under Bourbon rule* was true two centuries ago, but is not true now. But the judgment as it stands, without context, is in-completely stated. That France is (or was) under Bourbon rule in the year 1906 A.D. is for all time false; that France is (or was) under Bourbon rule in the year 1706 A.D. is for all time true'.[1]

Keynes goes on from this to cite Bosanquet's distinction between the time *of* predication and the time *in* predication; but it may be doubted whether the influence of Bosanquet was really the para-mount one here. For ·Keynes wrote towards the end of a period of controversy on this point which had arisen not among traditional logicians but among the exponents (including two of Keynes's closest associates, Venn and Johnson) of the new 'logical algebra' of Boole. Boole himself began it. Having developed a symbolic calculus for handling relations of inclusion between classes, he found it equally well adapted to handling relations of implication between propositions, and asked himself why. In *The Laws of Thought*[2] he gave the answer that to say that X implies Y is to say in effect that the times at which X is true are wholly included in the times at which Y is true. Not that Boole's version of the propositional calculus is a logic of tenses; he does not in fact mention them, and has no symbolic form in his calculus even for 'p at t'; he simply takes each propositional symbol to stand for the time at which the

[1] J. N. Keynes, *Studies and Exercises in Formal Logic*, 4th ed. (1906), pp. 76–77.
[2] G. Boole, *An Investigation of the Laws of Thought* (1853), ch. xi.

proposition symbolized is true. But Venn observed that in applying Boole's account of this interpretation to particular cases, tense-distinctions would need to be considered.

> Consider first the case of a proposition in the present tense, referring to some event or occurrence which continues to happen during a certain portion of time. The most natural meaning (of Boole's suggestion) . . . would be to suppose someone incessantly repeating a proposition in the present tense, e.g. 'it rains', and to recognize this statement as true whenever rain was actually falling, and as false whenever it was not. . . . Take next the case of an event which is supposed to have happened . . . or is expected to happen . . ., the corresponding proposition being in the appropriate tense. . . . Let X stand for 'Francis wrote the Junius letters' and Y for 'Francis will be proved to be the author'. . . . If we are to take as our test the time during which any one could have accepted the propositions in the tense in which they stand, then X is true (if true at all) since 1769; and Y from that date up to some unknown date in the future.[1]

This passage brings out extremely clearly the connexion between the view that truth-values may change with time and the view that tenses are of logical interest, though in the nineteenth century the two points were emphasized quite separately by Boole and by Mill.

Venn was not happy, however, about the special importance which Boole attached to time. He granted that in the case of 'events which happen continuously through certain portions of time' we can 'consider the proposition as "true" during the time only when the events to which it refers are happening, and "false" at all other times'. But there is nothing peculiar to time in this; for 'we can do just the same in respect of place; the proposition being considered true *where* it rains, and false where it does not' (using his earlier example). And with regard to singular events which common speech will refer to at one time in one tense and at another time in another, Venn felt that 'if the event really happened as stated, then . . . we ought to regard the proposition as being always and everywhere "true": grammatical distinctions of tense being laid aside'.[2] Johnson was still more emphatic. In his first 1892 article on *The Logical Calculus* (to which Keynes was much indebted), he makes a general protest against those (including Venn) who

> identify (for symbolic purposes) the implication relation between two propositions with the relation between the subject-term and predicate-term of the universal categorical. . . . The universal categorical, 'All cases of A are cases of B', contemplates a number of different cases in which A or B may be found. . . . But (in) the hypothetical, implicational

[1] J. Venn, *Symbolic Logic*, 2nd ed. (1894), p. 451.   [2] Ibid., p. 452.

or inferential synthesis 'If the proposition A is true, the proposition B is true' . . . there is no differentiation of cases or times by which the propositions A and B can be said to be 'in some cases' or 'sometimes' true and 'in other cases' or 'at other times' false. The same proposition cannot be sometimes true and sometimes false.[1]

And in a footnote to this he says,

Those symbolists who deny this confuse the 'time during which the proposition is true' with the 'time to which the proposition explicitly or implicitly refers'. Propositions referring to different times are different propositions.

One of the writers against whom these remarks were directed, Hugh MacColl, was criticized on the same score in 1906 by Russell. The relevant portion of Russell's review[2] deserves to stand beside the Keynes quote as a *locus classicus* for the position it expresses.

Mr. MacColl . . . distinguishes five classes of statements: true, false, certain, impossible, variable. . . . A *variable* is defined as follows: 'When I say "A is sometimes true and sometimes false", or "A is *variable*", I merely mean that the symbol, word, or collection of words, denoted by A, sometimes represents a truth and sometimes an untruth.' As an instance he gives 'Mrs. Brown is not at home'. Here it is plain that what is variable primarily is the meaning of the form of words. What is expressed by the form of words at any given instant is not itself variable; but at another instant something else, itself equally invariable, is expressed by the same form of words. Similarly in other cases. The statement 'He is a barrister' expresses a truth in some contexts and a falsehood in others. Thus the variability involved is primarily in the meaning of the form of words. Ordinary language employs, for the sake of convenience, many words whose meaning varies with the context or with the time when they are employed; thus statements using such words must be supplemented by further data before they become unambiguous. It is such forms of words that constitute Mr. MacColl's 'variables'. But is not this importing into logic the defects of common speech? One of the objects to be aimed at in using symbols is that they should be free from the ambiguities of ordinary language. When we are told 'Mrs. Brown is not at home', we know the time at which this is said, and therefore we know what is meant. But in order to express explicitly the whole of what is meant, it is necessary to add the date, and then the statement is no longer 'variable' but always true or always false. . . . It is essential that logic should employ only forms of words which are unambiguous, and when this is done 'variable' statements disappear.

[1] W. E. Johnson, 'The Logical Calculus', *Mind*, 1892; first article, § 9.
[2] *Mind*, 1906, pp. 256–7. I owe this reference to Mr. P. T. Geach's review of Mates's *Stoic Logic* in the *Philosophical Review*, Jan. 1955.

Something not unlike them, however, may properly occur even in a symbolic system; for, Russell goes on,

> 'There is . . . a further distinction, namely that between propositions and propositional functions; and in regard to the latter, Mr. MacColl's distinction of *certain*, *impossible* and *variable* does seem to be applicable. We may say that '*x* is a barrister' or 'Mrs. Brown is not at home at the time *x*' is true for some values of *x* and false for others. Either of these is a propositional function; but neither is a proposition. Each is merely a general form into which many propositions fit, namely all those resulting from giving values to *x*. Such a form may be called a *certainty* when it is 'true for all values of *x*', i.e. when, whatever value we give to *x*, the resulting *proposition* is true; it is *impossible* when it is 'false for all values of *x*', and *variable* when it is neither certain nor impossible. Thus we shall say that *true* and *false* are alone applicable to propositions, while *certain*, *variable* and *impossible* are applicable to ambiguous forms of words and to propositional functions.

It cannot be denied that a very brilliant and useful piece of analysis is performed by Russell here; and MacColl was certainly wrong in treating 'true', 'false', and 'sometimes true and sometimes false' as if they all came out of the same box. (There is an echo here of the error by which Boole made the calculus of 'times of truth' a *substitute* for an ordinary calculus of truth-functions—that is, in my view, a calculus of functions whose *truth-value at a given time* depends on the *truth-value at that time* of their arguments. A logic in which we quantify over times cannot replace this but presupposes it.) The important question, however, is whether Russell is not himself at fault in treating 'true this morning but false this afternoon' (which we might say of 'Mrs. Brown is not at home') as coming out of the same box as 'true of Mr. Smith but false of Mr. Jones' (which we might say of 'He is a barrister'). Here Russell clearly shares Venn's feeling, in his difference from Boole, that there is nothing special about time. I propose to discuss this point in some detail, but first the history must be brought up to date.

Standing somewhat apart from the logicians mentioned hitherto, but too important to pass unnoticed, was Charles Sanders Peirce. Peirce had no formalized logic of time-distinctions, but this was for him a matter of expediency rather than of principle; he wrote in about 1903,

> *Time* has usually been considered by logicians to be what is called 'extra-logical' matter. I have never shared this opinion. But I have thought that logic had not yet reached the state of development at which the introduction of temporal modifications of its forms would not result in great confusion; and I am much of that way of thinking yet.[1]

[1] C. S. Peirce, *Collected Papers*, 4. 523.

His unformalized reflections on the subject are, however, often illuminating. A constant feature of his thought is a close association of time with modality. The passage just cited, for instance, occurs in a discussion of the possible considered as that which, in a given state of information, is not known to be false. A full treatment of modalities thus conceived, Peirce suggests, must take account of alterations in the state of information presupposed; we must be able to formulate, for example, the law that *after p* has been incorporated in our information, the falsehood of *p* is not 'possible'.[1] And more than that, we must eventually take account of revisions and corrections of our 'information'—but it is at this point that Peirce says that the time is not ripe for such developments.

This subjective and relative sense was frequently assigned to modal words by Peirce, and he seems to have found them easier to deal with that way. (He liked to say, for example, that a purely assertoric logic is the modal logic of an omniscient being, for whom the only 'possible' state of affairs is the actual one.)[2] He was insistent, however, that this cannot be the whole story about modality; there are real possibilities and necessities which are independent of anyone's state of information.[3] And here too he found the distinction of past and future highly relevant, his thought being at this point reminiscent of, and indeed consciously indebted to, that of Aristotle and the scholastic logicians. The past, he says more than once, is 'the sum of *faits accomplis*';[4] 'I have considerable *power* over the future, but nobody except the Parisian mob imagines that he can change the past by much or by little'.[5] He does not, however, describe the past as being for that reason 'necessary' (which would not only have echoed the ancient view but would have been the objective analogue of his own theorem, in the field of 'subjective' modality, that *p* becomes 'necessary' after it has been added to our presupposed information). He prefers to say that the past is 'actual'; it is the area of 'brute fact'; 'necessity' is to be found rather in the realm of *law*, and the connexion of this with time is that law alone can extend reality to the future. 'Everything in the Future is either

[1] *Collected Papers*, 4. 518, 522.

[2] Ibid. 2. 347–8, 3. 442–4. Peirce, with Venn and MacColl, was among those upbraided by Johnson for 'identifying the implication relation between two propositions with the relation between the subject-term and predicate-term of the universal categorical'; and in these passages he defends this position by arguing that all conditionals contain an implicit quantification, over possible states of affairs if over nothing else, the assertoric calculus being the result of treating this 'universe' as one-membered. He says that a quantification over times *could* be introduced at this point, but need not be. Cf. also 4. 376, 385.

[3] Ibid. 5. 453 ff., 6. 367.   [4] Ibid. 5. 459; cf. 2. 84.

[5] Ibid. 6. 70; cf. 6. 127–31.

destined, i.e. necessitated already, or is *undecided*, the contingent future of Aristotle';[1] and he argues that if general laws were not as real as particular facts, not only contingent but even necessary propositions about the future would have no truth-value:

> A certain event either will happen or it will not. There is nothing now in existence to constitute the truth of its being about to happen, or of its being not about to happen, unless it be certain circumstances to which only a law or uniformity can lend efficacy. But that law or uniformity, the nominalists say, has no real being, it is only a mental representation. If so, neither the being about to happen nor the being about not to happen has any reality at present. . . . If, however, we admit that the law has a real being, and of the mode of being of an individual, but even more real, then the future necessary consequent of a present state of things is as real and true as the present state of things itself.[2]

The idea that the reality of the future, by contrast with the present and the past, is somehow non-individual, is developed in another way in what is perhaps the most suggestive of all the Peirce passages on our topic. Peirce often distinguished modal logic from other branches of the subject by its being concerned with different 'universes' from the universe of existent things, so that all theories of higher-order predicates and relations are in a way modal;[3] and this whole field was one which he was inclined to leave to his successors,[4] though he worked on portions of it in his later years. He surmised that in its main outlines it would not be very different from the logic of 'existential' relations, i.e. the lower predicate calculus, but he saw a difference emerging at one point at least. 'Every correlate of an existential relation is a single object'; 'The one logical universe, to which all the correlates of an existential relationship belong, is ultimately composed of *units*, or subjects';[5] but with the 'universes' which are presupposed in modal logic it is not as simple as this, and it is not as simple as this even with the extension of the universe of existents into the future. Towards the beginning of a paper (dated 1897) on various sorts of infinite multitude, Peirce brings out the difference in this way:

> Whether the constituent individuals or units of a collection have each of them a distinct identity of its own or not depends upon the nature of the universe of discourse. . . . As long as the discourse relates to a common objective and completed experience, those units *retain* each its distinct identity. If you and I talk of the great tragedians who have acted in New York within the last ten years, a definite list can be drawn

---

[1] Ibid. 5. 459.   [2] Ibid. 6. 368.
[3] Ibid. 3. 573–4, 606–8; 4. 431, 514, 546, 552 n, 553 n.
[4] Ibid. 6. 318–19.   [5] Ibid. 6. 318.

up of them, and each of them has his or her proper name. But suppose we open the question of how far the general influences of the theatrical world at present favour the development of female stars rather than of male stars. In order to discuss that, we have to go beyond our *completed* experience, . . . and have to consider the possible or probable stars of the immediate future. We can no longer assign proper names to each. The individual actors to which our discourse now relates become largely merged into general varieties; and their separate identities are partially lost. Again, statisticians can tell us pretty accurately how many people in the city of New York will commit suicide in the year after next. None of these persons have at present any idea of doing any such thing, and it is very doubtful whether it can properly be said to be determinate now who they will be, although their number is approximately fixed. There is an approach to a want of distinct identity in the individuals of the collection of persons who are to commit suicide in the year 1899.

Collections of future individuals, Peirce goes on to say, are in this respect like collections of possible individuals or of imaginary individuals.

When we say that of all possible throws of a pair of dice one thirty-sixth will show sixes, the collection of possible throws which have not been made is a collection of which the individual units have no distinct identity. It is impossible so to designate a single one of those possible throws that have not been thrown that the designation shall be applicable to only one definite possible throw; and this impossibility does not spring from any incapacity of ours, but from the fact that in their own nature those throws are not individually distinct. The possible is necessarily general and no amount of general specification can reduce a general class of possibilities to an individual case. It is only actuality, the force of existence, which bursts the fluidity of the general and produces a discrete unit. . . .

When the universe of discourse relates to a common experience, but this experience is of something imaginary, as when we discuss the world of Shakespeare's creation in the play of Hamlet, we find individual distinction existing so far as the work of imagination has carried it, while beyond that point there is vagueness and generality.[1]

The point of the reference to Hamlet is made more explicit in an earlier paper (of 1893).

If any profound and learned member of the German Shakespearian Society were to start the inquiry how long since Polonius had had his hair cut at the time of his death, perhaps the only reply that could be made would be that Polonius was nothing but a creature of Shakespeare's brain, and that Shakespeare never thought of the point raised.[2]

[1] *Collected Papers,* 4. 172.   [2] Ibid. 4. 61.

This passage and the last one take us some distance from time and tenses, but the substitution in them of 'future' for 'possible' and 'imaginary' will make their bearing plain enough. Peirce himself continues the last-quoted passage as follows:

> It is certainly conceivable that this world which we call the real world is not perfectly real but that there are things similarly indeterminate. We cannot be sure that it is not so.

And it seems that he came to believe, with Aristotle, that this *is* the case with 'this world which we call the real world' so far as it is still future. (In the terminology of Meinong,[1] even concrete existents are to this extent 'incomplete objects'.)

In this discussion of different 'universes' there is an echo of medieval theories of *ampliatio*, though Peirce does not refer explicitly to these, and its seems to me of some importance for the historian to determine how far the schoolmen anticipated his perception of this want of individual identity in *possibilia*, etc. (for when this point is appreciated the doctrine is much more acceptable). Part of what he says could be expressed by saying that 'It will be the case two years hence that approximately n New Yorkers commit suicide' does not entail 'There are approximately n New Yorkers who are going to commit suicide two years hence'; but when he does discuss the relation between forms of this sort—in connexion with ordinary modality—he seems to mistake the real bearing of his theory. In his article on 'Modality' in Baldwin's *Dictionary of Philosophy and Psychology* he says

> In the necessary particular proposition and the possible universal proposition there is sometimes a distinction between the 'composite' and 'divided' senses. 'Some S must be P', taken in the composite sense, means that there is no case, in the whole range of ignorance, where some S or other is not P; but taken in the divided sense, it means that there is some S which same S remains P throughout the whole range of ignorance. . . . When there is any such distinction, the divided sense asserts more than the composite in necessary particular propositions, and less in possible universal. But in most cases the individuals do not remain identifiable throughout the range of possibility, when the distinction falls to the ground. It never applies to necessary universal propositions or to possible particular propositions.[2]

From the last sentence it is clear that Peirce accepts the Barcan formula, and from the preceding sentence it would seem that on his view the non-identifiability of *possibilia*, so far from introducing

---

[1] See J. N. Findlay, *Meinong's Theory of Objects*, ch. vi. Meinong, of course, did not himself admit that concrete existents are 'incomplete objects' even to this extent.

[2] Peirce, *Collected Papers*, 2. 382.

a new distinction between 'Possibly something ϕ's' and 'Something possibly ϕ's', obliterates the old one between 'Necessarily something ϕ's' and 'Something necessarily ϕ's'. It was a very great deal, however, for him to have seen a difficulty at this point; and, by and large, his insights into the relations between actuality, possibility, time, and individual identity are still waiting to be adequately formalized.

Returning to the main stream, formal logicians since 1906 have taken pretty consistently the Keynes-Johnson-Russell line about time, but there has lately been a certain straining at the Russellian leash, most notably perhaps in the work of Mr. P. F. Strawson.[1] Mr. Strawson's anti-Russellianism, however, like the anti-Aristotelianism of Peter Ramus, looks much less radical on careful inspection than it does at first glance. He does not propose a *logic* of tense-distinctions, except in a very trivial sense of the word; rather, he adduces tense-distinctions as something important which formal logic cannot handle. (And with this, apart from the 'important', his main Russellian critic, Professor Quine, agrees.)[2] Nor does he contend that there are statements which are true at one time and false at another. What he prefers to say is that the same *sentence* may be used to make a true statement on some occasions and a false statement on others. This is almost pure Russell—compare the distinction, in the review of MacColl, between the one 'form of words' and the various things which are in different contexts 'expressed' by it. Russell's protest, a little farther on, against 'importing into logic the defects of common speech', is hardly in the Strawsonian manner; but only too often Mr. Strawson seems less concerned to learn from common speech than to protect it, and in protecting common speech from the onslaughts of formal logic he incidentally protects formal logic from the onslaughts of common speech. This is a pity, because the main use of common speech is to draw the formal logician's attention to fields of inquiry —of his own sort of inquiry—which he has so far neglected.

Mr. Strawson points out that in finding actual statements which exemplify the 'forms' of statement whose entailment relations the formal logician studies, it does not suffice (except perhaps in certain favoured cases) to replace symbols by words of the appropriate sort; for the result of such substitution will often not make a statement at all unless it is *used* in particular circumstances in a particular way, and *what* statement it makes will often depend on the occasion on which it is used. When it comes to its actual application, therefore,

[1] P. F. Strawson, *Introduction to Logical Theory* (1952). See especially pp. 150-1, 214.
[2] W. V. Quine, 'Mr. Strawson on Logical Theory', *Mind*, Oct. 1953, pp. 440-3.

the 'theory of entailment' must be supplemented by a 'theory of reference'. And it is to this 'theory of reference', according to Mr. Strawson, that the study of tenses belongs, along with the study of words like 'here', 'there', 'he', 'this', 'I', etc. Formally, it would seem, there is nothing special about time in Mr. Strawson's logic any more than there is in Russell's or Venn's.

Is there, then, anything special about time? That is the principal question which all this history puts to us,[1] and I conclude by offering the following somewhat technical reflections upon it: Consider the three remarks

'It was raining last Saturday.'
'It is raining in Dunedin.'
'My dog is ill.'

One theory about the logical structure of these statements[2] would be expressed by rewording them thus (with a line to indicate the main point of analysis):

'It was the case last Saturday that / it is raining.'
'It is the case in Dunedin that / it is raining.'
'It is the case with my dog that / he is ill.'

In this analysis the statements are represented as being of the form Txp, where T is a dyadic operator of the form 'It is (was) the case on (in, with) – – – that – – – ', having for its first argument some sort of name (of a time, of a place, of an individual) and for its second argument a statement, or something very like a statement. The other main theory about the logical structure of the given statements is that which would be expressed by rewording them thus:

'Last Saturday / falls into the class of rainy days.'
'Dunedin / is being subjected to rainy weather.'
'My dog / is ill.'

Here the statements are represented as being of the form ϕx, where some noun x is the subject of a verb or verb-equivalent ϕ; the verb has, moreover, no appearance of containing a statement in itself, and it may be contended that what appears to be a statement in the Txp form is in fact something less than that.

---

[1] Its importance was first brought home to me by Mr. J. M. Shorter, who has a pleasant habit of trying to push me farther than I want to go. The 'try it out and see' method of answering the question 'why not do these things with space, etc., as well as time?' was suggested by my wife.

[2] I am not now attempting to adhere to Mr. Strawson's use of this word. In ordinary speech, so far as I can see, the word 'statement' is used at least as often for *a sentence in use* as for something which the sentence is being 'used to make'.

Now it is fairly clear that any statement whatever of the form ϕx can be inflated to something of the form Txp by finding within the verb ϕ something which can be thought of as a statement, if necessary in some rather extended sense of 'statement'. Thus far, there is indeed nothing special about time. And conversely, any statement of the form Txp is already of the form ϕx (is already a propositional function of x), being the special case of that form in which ϕ is $T'p$; and in at least some contexts no logical purpose is served by analysing the ϕ into the operator T and the other argument p, and ordinary speech may well contain expressions for ϕ as a whole in which no parts correspond exactly to the T and the p of this analysis. If, with a given type of x (times, places, individuals) and a given associated T, the analysis of ϕx into Txp serves no logical purpose in *any* context, we may describe this particular Txp form as 'collapsible' into the ϕx form. And if it should turn out that with 'It is the case at the place x that —' and 'It is the case with the individual x that —' the Txp form is collapsible whereas with 'It is the case at the time x that —' it is not, there is every ground for holding that in the latter cases the Txp form brings out distinct structural features of statements, and at least some ground for holding that in the former cases we have to do with nothing more than a verbal artifice.

It is not difficult to give a more precise account of this notion of being 'collapsible', which is plainly crucial here. If the form Txp is (for a given type of x) collapsible, then it must be possible to treat the p which occurs in it as standing for a type of expression which is not a statement on its own, but is a mere part of a ϕ, which itself only forms a statement when an x is attached to it. All the rest follows from this. Firstly, if we are to be able to treat our p's in this way, we must be able to say that whenever a p is used in our Tx calculus without a Tx governing it,[1] as if it could stand for a complete statement in its own, this is because there is some Tx 'understood'. (An exponent of a collapsible tense-logic, for example, will say that the plain 'It is raining', if it expresses a statement at all, does so because some definite date *at* which it is raining—the date of utterance—is understood by both speaker and hearer, and similarly with place.) Formally, this means that a collapsible Tx calculus must contain as a law the formula $\Sigma x E p Txp$, asserting with respect to any p that there is some x such that the plain p is equivalent to Txp.

Secondly, if we refuse to take seriously the propositional status

---

[1] Directly or indirectly—the p in $TxCpq$ is of course 'governed' by the Tx before the whole implication. Not, however, the p in $CpTxq$.

of the p's of a Tx calculus, all iterated Tx-ings, as in $TyTxp$, must
be reducible to single ones. For it is only when Txp and p are on
the same logical level—both equally 'propositional'—that it can
be an equally significant move to attach Tx or Ty to either of them.
The point will be quite obvious if we try to 'collapse' the form
$TyTxp$ as it stands. Txp gives ϕx, so $TyTxp$ gives ϕxy; but in the
collapsing of Txp we assume that our ϕ is monadic, so that the
adding of a y after its argument can add nothing significant. For
instance, 'It is the case with your dog that it is the case with my dog
that he is ill', collapsed as it stands, would yield 'Your dog my dog
is ill'; what function can 'Your dog' serve here? This example suggests one way in which this condition can be met— it is met if in the
form $TyTxp$ the Ty can be regarded as 'vacuous', i.e. if $TyTxp$ is
always equivalent to the plain Txp. (For example, 'It was the case
on Friday that it would be the case on Saturday that it is raining'
to 'It was the case on Saturday that it is raining'; 'It is the case in
Christchurch that it is the case in Dunedin that it is raining' to 'It
is the case in Dunedin that it is raining'; and 'It is the case with
your dog that it is the case with my dog that he is ill' to 'It is the
case with my dog that he is ill'.)

But even when the collapsing cannot be done as simply as this,
it can sometimes still be done nevertheless. Consider, for example,
a place-logic in which we have the means of formulating the law

'If it is the case (here) that p, then it is the case n miles away to the left
   that it is the case n miles away to the right that p'.

Using the form Lnp for 'It is the case n miles away to the left that
p', and Rnp similarly for 'right', this law would be symbolized as
$CpLnRnp$. And if we regarded this L–R logic as a Tx logic with n
for x and L and R for two types of T, and knew of no way of eliminating double Tx-ing but that of treating all of a sequence of Tx
prefixes but the one next to p as vacuous, we would conclude that
place-logic is not collapsible. For the accumulation of L–R opera-
tions is certainly not vacuous in this logic—$LmRn$, and even $RmRn$,
are certainly not equivalent to the simple Rn. It seems clear, however, that what we have in this case is not a simple Tx logic, but
something representable as a Tx logic in which our x's are given,
not directly, but by means of a *name-forming operator on intervals*. Our
x's are of the form λn, where this means 'the place n miles to the
left', with Lnp for $T\lambda np$ with positive values of n and Rnp for $T\lambda np$
with negative values of n. And although we cannot equate

'It is the case m miles to the left that it is the case n miles to the left that p'
   ($T\lambda m T\lambda np$)

with

'It is the case n miles to the left that p'

($T\lambda np$), we *can* equate it with *something* of the form $T\lambda lp$, namely the $T\lambda lp$ in which l is the algebraic sum of m and n (with a wider range of directions, the vector sum).

As a genuine example of a Tx logic in which this condition of collapsibility is not met we may take a tense-logic in which λn means 'the time n days back', Pnp is defined as $U\lambda np$ for positive and Fnp as $U\lambda np$ for negative values of n, and in which we assign to future contingents a third truth-value. For in such a system we cannot equate

'It was the case $m+n$ days ago that it will be the case n days hence that p',

i.e. $PSmnFnp$, or $U\lambda(m+n)U\lambda(-n)p$, with

'It was the case m days ago that p',

i.e. Pmp, or $U\lambda mp$. For even if it was the case m days ago that p, it might not have been true $m+n$ days ago that it was going to be the case n days later that p, for $m+n$ days ago the issue might still have been indeterminate. But if $U\lambda(m+n)U\lambda(-n)$ were equivalent to any single $U\lambda$ prefix it would clearly be to $U\lambda m$. So this condition of collapsibility cannot be met by this type of tense-logic.

A third part of the criterion for collapsibility is that where δ is any n-adic truth-operator, and $p_1, ..., p_n$ contain no x, the formulae

$$Tx\delta p_1 ... p_n$$

and
$$\delta Txp_1 ... Txp_n$$

must be equivalent. (For example, with the monadic operator N, $TxNp$ must be equivalent to $NTxp$; with the dyadic C, $TxCpq$ must be equivalent to $CTxpTxq$.) For the collapsing of both these formulae would give us

$$\delta\phi \, x ... \phi_n x,$$

so that if the originals were not equivalent, our collapsing process could lead to contradictions. For example, in the Utp calculus underlying our tense-logical System Q, $NUtp$ is not equivalent to, and does not even imply, $UtNp$, so that we could in consistency with this calculus affirm something of the form

$$KNUtpNUtNp.$$

But the above steps will turn this into the contradiction

$$KN\phi tNN\phi t.$$

(It might be argued that we could keep our original distinction between $NUtp$ and $UtNp$, and preserve the $KN\phi tNN\phi t$ form from contradiction, by using brackets, thus: $N(\phi t)$, $(N\phi)t$; $KN(\phi t)N(N\phi)t$. But when brackets are taken so seriously that you can do all this with them, they have become simply a notational variant of the operator U, and no genuine collapsing of the Utp form has been effected.)

These conditions of collapsibility are not sufficient, as there are further types of Tx formulae which they do not take care of; but they are all necessary and will do to indicate the kind of features which a Tx system must have if it is to be collapsible. And so far as I can see, we have no reason for not incorporating the full conditions of collapsibility—certainly we have none for not incorporating those listed above—in a calculus in which Txp is interpreted as 'It is the case at the place x that p' or 'It is the case with the individual x that p'; whereas we do have reasons (though their weight is not easy to assess) for denying some of these conditions when Txp is interpreted as 'It is (was, will be) the case at the time x that p'. The Fn calculus of our Lecture II, and Ut calculus of III, do appear to be collapsible, and indeed it is easy to reinterpret these calculi as place-logics.[1] But these were the tense-logics of our age of innocence; they have not survived inspection.

With regard to individual-logics, I should add that while 'It is the case with x that p' is obviously a collapsible T-function of x, *intentional* functions of individuals (such as 'x wishes that p', 'x believes that p', 'x asserts that p') are just as obviously *non*-collapsible; and it is of interest that before Łoś introduced his Utp calculus for formalizing Mill's canons he discussed a 'logic of assertion' with a very similar structure, with the form Lxp for 'x asserts that p'.[2] I am not at all happy about the particular postulates Łoś uses; for example, he has 'Everyone asserts that p' implying p (this being an axiom) and p implying 'Someone asserts that p' (provable),[3] whereas it seems to me that these must definitely be rejected in any satisfactory intentional logic, with the consequence that such a logic cannot meet even the first condition of collapsibility, the presence of the theorem $\Sigma xEpTxp$. But in the

---

[1] These two systems illustrate a theorem which is easily provable for collapsible Tx systems generally, namely that if Requirement 2 is met by the vacuity (in accumulated Tx-ings) of all Tx's but the one next to p, $\Pi xTxp$ and $\Sigma xTxp$ will be an L and M conforming to Lewis's S5, while if Requirement 2 is met, but not in this way, $\Pi xTxp$ and $\Sigma xTxp$ will be an L and M conforming to S4.

[2] Polish paper reviewed by R. Suszko in the *Journal of Symbolic Logic*, vol. xiv (1949), pp. 64–65. See also my *Formal Logic*, appendix i, System 13.1.

[3] This makes ΠxLx and ΣxLx a pair of modal functions in the sense of Łukasiewicz.

present context Łoś's actual postulates are a matter of minor importance[1]—he has found, as no one before him seems to have found, an appropriate symbolism for this type of subject-matter, and he sees that the logic of dates and intervals and the logic of assertion both require a symbolism of this kind. There is something special about time; but not so special that it provides the only non-collapsible Tx logics there can be.

[1] On this side—the side of the actual postulates—there is much more promise in the 'Q-logics' of von Wright's important paper 'On the Logic of some Axiological and Epistemological Concepts', *Eripainos Ajatus*, vol. xvii (1952), pp. 213–34.

Some Features of the Lewis Modal Systems, and Further Comparisons with Q and Ł

THE Lewis modal systems,[1] with the system T of Feys (equivalent to S2 with the rule to infer $L\alpha$ from α), may be arranged in the following diagram:

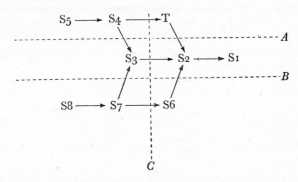

An arrow indicates that the system to the left contains all theorems in the system to the right, and more besides. Systems above the dotted line A contain the rule to infer $L\alpha$ from α, and systems below this line do not contain it.[2] Systems below the line B contain as a law the formula MMp, and systems above this line do not. These two features are incompatible, for (1) if everything is possibly possible (MMp) then nothing is necessarily necessary ($NLLp$), for if anything could not but be necessary its opposite could not be possible; but (2) if from any thesis α we may infer $L\alpha$ as a new thesis, then by the same rule we may infer $LL\alpha$ from $L\alpha$, so that all formulae of the form $LL\alpha$ in which α expresses a logical law must themselves be admitted as logical laws, and therefore as true. The system Q is like those below the line A in not containing the rule to infer $L\alpha$ from α, but it is like those above it in not only not containing but being incompatible with S6–8; for it does contain

---

[1] The postulate-sets associated with them may be found in my *Formal Logic*, appendix i, 6.1–6.3.
[2] This is proved for S3 (and by implication for S1–2) in W. T. Parry's 'Modalities in the *Survey* system of strict implication', *JSL*, vol. v (1939), pp. 137–54, sect. vi. 1. S3 contains $LCpp$ but not $LLCpp$.

the rule to infer $NMN\alpha$ from α, and so to obtain $NMNNMN\alpha$, i.e. $NMMN\alpha$, from $NMN\alpha$, and from α; and $NMMN\alpha$ directly contradicts $MMN\alpha$, which would be derivable by substitution from MMp if this were a law.

The systems to the left of the line C are distinguished by having a finite number of non-equivalent modalities, meaning by a modality a sequence of prefixes containing only N's, L's, and M's, with the null sequence as a limiting case. S5 contains the reduction theses $CMpLMp$ and $CMLpLp$, which enable us (with the help of their converses, which follow from $CLpp$ and $CpMp$) to equate any sequence of L's and M's with the last item alone (e.g. $LLMLMLLM$ with the plain M). Hence in this system the only non-equivalent modes are the six Lp, p, Mp, NMp, Np, and NLp. In S4 (which has $CMMpMp$ but not $CMLpLp$, and $CLpLLp$ but not $CMpLMp$) these six enlarge to fourteen, namely those in the following diagram of entailments, and their negations:[1]

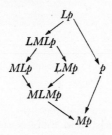

In S3 (which does not contain $CMMpMp$ but does turn out to contain, as a theorem, $CMMMpMMp$), the number enlarges to forty-two, namely those in the following diagram of entailments, and their negations:[2]

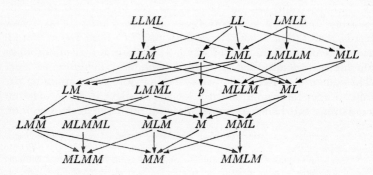

[1] W. T. Parry, op. cit. vi. 1.   [2] Ibid., sect. iv.

Of the systems to the *right* of the line *C*, it has been established[1] that there are an infinity of non-equivalent modes in S1, S2, and T, and I would conjecture that this is also true of S6, though there is not very much known about the three systems (S6–8) with *MMp* as a law. S7 and S8, since they contain S3, will contain all reduction theses of the latter, and therefore no larger number of modalities.

The system Q at this point resembles the Lewis systems to the *left* of our line *C*; that is, it has a finite number of non-equivalent modalities. The number of them is in fact fourteen, though not the fourteen of S4, but the following (with their negations):

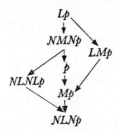

To facilitate the proof that these are all, we may make use of the following tables based on the 6-valued matrix used in Chapter V (since at this point the 6-valued matrix gives the same results as the infinite one):

p	Lp	Mp	$NMNp$	$NLNp$	LMp	$NLNLp$
1	1	1	1	1	1	1
2	5	2	2	2	5	2
3	6	1	6	1	1	6
4	6	1	6	1	1	6
5	5	5	5	2	5	2
6	6	6	6	6	6	6

If we could proceed from *L* to stronger modalities, we would start with *LL*, *NMNL*, and *LNMN*; but these are all equivalent to *L*. The one form which might be thought to be between *L* and *NMN*, namely *NMNNMN*, is equivalent to *NMN*. If we could construct ever-more-elaborate modes between *L* and *M* in strength, we would begin with *ML*, *LM*, *M(NMN)*, *(NMN)M*, *(NLN)L*, and *L(NLN)*; but *ML* is equivalent to *L*, *MNMN* to *NMN*,

[1] J. C. C. McKinsey, 'Proof that there are infinitely many modalities in Lewis's system S2', *JSL*, v (1940), pp. 110–12; B. Sobociński, 'Note on a Modal System of Feys–von Wright', *Journal of Computing Systems*, vol. i, No. 3 (July 1953), Paper 13 (Sect. 2).

$NMNM$ to M, and $LNLN$ to LM. LM and $NLNL$, however, are not equivalent to L, to M or to one another, though we cannot obtain from either of them new forms which are as it were on a level with L and NMN but independent of both. For

$$L(LM) = NMN(LM) = LM;$$
$$(LM)L = (LM)NMN = L;$$
$$L(NLNL) = L;$$
$$(NLNL)L = (NLNL)NMN = NMN(NLNL) = NLNL.$$

Nor do we obtain anything new by iterating LM or $NLNL$; for $LMLM = LM$ and $NLNLNLNL = NLNL$. Nor by weakening them to modes which might be on a level with M or NLN but independent of both; for

$$M(LM) = (LM)M = (LM)NLN = LM; \qquad NLN(LM) = NLN;$$
$$M(NLNL) = NLN(NLNL) = NLNL;$$
$$(NLNL)M = (NLNL)NLN = NLN.$$

The form which might be thought to be between Mp and $NLNp$, namely MMp, is equivalent to Mp; and forms which might be thought weaker than $NLNp$ are disposed of by the equations

$$MNLNp = NLNMp = NLNNLNp = NLNp.$$

And all these results will be found to accord intuitively with our original tense-logical interpretation of Q.

The Ł-modal system of Łukasiewicz fits into this picture as follows: Like S1–3, it has neither the rule to infer $L\alpha$ from α nor the law MMp, but unlike them it is not merely consistent with both without implying either but positively inconsistent with both. And like S5 it has only six non-equivalent modalities, and the same six, but the method of reduction is different. A sequence of L's and M's is equivalent not to the last item alone but to the first alone, e.g. $LLMLMMLMp$ not to Mp but to Lp. But the main difference between the Ł-modal system and all the Lewis systems is that it has a 4-valued characteristic matrix, whereas no Lewis system (or T) has a finite characteristic matrix. That Q also has no finite characteristic matrix can be shown by the following adaptation of Dugundji's proof[1] that there is none for S1–6:

---

[1] James Dugundji, 'Note on a property of matrices for Lewis and Langford's calculi of propositions', *JSL*, vol. v (1940), pp. 150–1. Dugundji states that his proof was suggested by Gödel's proof that there is no finite characteristic matrix for Heyting's propositional calculus in C, N, A, and K.

Suppose we have a matrix involving n 'values' (n being finite) equivalent to the infinite matrix given for Q. Consider the series of formulae (in which $E'pq = NMNEpq$):

$E'pq$

$AAE'pqE'prE'qr$

$AAAAAE'pqE'prE'psE'qrE'qsE'rs,$

etc., and let $F(n+1)$ be the formula in this series which has $n+1$ different propositional variables. As there are only n values to go round $n+1$ variables, any assignment of values will in at least one case give the same value to two different variables. Hence at least one of the alternants will have the value that $E'pp$ would have for some value of p, and the whole will always have one of the possible values of $AE'ppq$. But if the n-valued matrix is really equivalent to that for Q, the value of $AE'ppq$ will always be a designated one (since $AE'ppq$ is a thesis of Q). Hence $F(n+1)$ will be verified by the matrix. But in our infinite matrix for Q, it is possible to assign to any collection of $n+1$ variables p, q, r, s, etc., the following values:

$$p = \text{IIIIIIIIIII, etc.,}$$

$$q = \text{I3IIIIIIIII, etc.,}$$

$$r = \text{II3IIIIIIII, etc.,}$$

$$s = \text{III3IIIIIII, etc.,}$$

and so on (moving the 3 along one place each time). Hence with every one of the alternants $E'pq$, $E'pr$, etc., the sequence for the first argument will have a I where the sequence for the second has a 3; the sequence for Epq (or Epr, etc.) will therefore contain a 3 at that point, and the sequence for $E'pq$, or $NMNEpq$, will be that consisting of 3's only. Hence the sequence for the alternation of all these will be that consisting of 3's only, so that for this assignment of values the value of $F(n+1)$ will be an undesignated one. Hence $F(n+1)$ will not be verified by the infinite matrix, and our n-valued matrix (with n finite) will not be equivalent to it.

The following is a further respect in which Q resembles the Lewis systems and differs from the Ł-modal: All the Lewis systems, T, Q, and Ł contain as a proper part the classical assertoric propositional calculus. At least, they all contain it when it is formulated with no variables but propositional ones. But only the Ł-modal system contains it in the form of what Leśniewski called 'prototothetic', i.e. with not only propositional variables but also variables which can stand for proposition-forming *operators* on propositions. In this form it might have for its sole axiom $C\delta pC\delta Np\delta q$ ('If any function of p, then if also that function of not-p, then that function of anything at all'), with C and N undefined; or its axiom might be $C\delta\delta o\delta p$, with C and o undefined, and Np defined as Cpo; or it might be $C\delta pCq\delta\delta q$, with C and Π undefined (and o defined as Πpp), and with Łukasiewicz's rules for Π added to those of substitution and detachment. In all these forms, and also with Leśniewski's own axiomatizations (different from any of these), protothetic contains as a thesis the 'law of extensionality' $CEpqC\delta p\delta q$, 'If p and q have the same truth-value then any function of p implies that same function of q'. And so long as it is only the assertoric propositional calculus with which we have to do, i.e. so long as the only constant operators available to be substituted for δ are ones forming 2-valued truth-functions, we need have no misgivings about this law or about postulates which entail it.

When, however, the proposition-forming operators on propositions which a system contains include L and M, we must in general either abandon postulates of this sort or explicitly exclude modal operators from the range of values of δ. The exception is the Ł-modal system, in which $C\delta pC\delta Np\delta q$ is one of the axioms, and modal operators are substitutable for δ, so that $CMpCMNpMq$ ('If p is possible, then if not-p is also possible, anything is possible') is a law. But $CMpCMNpMq$, and therefore $C\delta pC\delta Np\delta q$ (unless the range of δ is restricted) do not hold in the Lewis systems, in T or in Q.[1] Nor does $CEpqCMpMq$ (and so not $CEpqC\delta p\delta q$); for if p and q are both false, but p possible and q impossible (something which can happen in these systems), Epq and Mp will be true but Mq false.

This difference is quite radical, but it should be added that even in the Ł-modal system there is *something like* the dilemma of dropping $C\delta pC\delta Np\delta q$ or restricting the range of δ. We may put it this way: In the pure assertoric calculus the restriction on the range of δ when laws like $C\delta pC\delta Np\delta q$ are laid down for it is in a sense *present but not felt*, because this calculus contains no operators in this category for which such laws do not hold. The latter is true of the Ł-modal system also, but the restriction begins nevertheless to be felt now; for $C\delta pC\delta Np\delta q$ continues to hold only because *either* we are using (not δ but) M and its derivatives as variable operators which vary only over a part even of the range available within the calculus, *or* the calculus is a 4-valued one which is functionally incomplete, i.e. there are 4-valued truth-operators which are not definable within

---

[1] In any system but Łukasiewicz's, $CMpCMNpMq$ would entail $CMpp$, thus: $CMpCMNpMq \rightarrow CMpCMNpMKpNp$ (subst. $q/KpNp$); this with

$$NMKpNp \rightarrow CMpNMNp \rightarrow CMpp.$$

But in Ł there are no theses of the form $NM\alpha$, such as $NMKpNp$.

it. There are 256 non-equivalent monadic 4-valued truth-operators, but only sixteen of them are definable in Ł. We cannot, for example, define in Ł an operator X such that $Xp = 1, 1, 1, 4$ when $p = 1, 2, 3, 4$. And in a 4-valued calculus which *is* functionally complete $C\delta p C\delta N p \delta q$ must go; for with Łukasiewicz's tables for C and N, $CXpCXNpXq = 4$ for $p = 3$ and $q = 4$. (The tables are the same as the 4-valued ones for C and N which were used at the end of Chapter II; and with these, $CX3CXN3X4 = C1CX24 = C1C14 = C14 = 4$.) $CEpqC\delta p\delta q$ fails for the same values of δ, p, and q. In fact I do not know of any system containing this law which has not at least one of the following three limitations: Either (i) the system is 2-valued, or (ii) it is functionally incomplete, or (iii) it does not contain all the classical laws for C and E. An example of the third type would be a functionally complete 3-valued system in which the C and E of the law $CEpqC\delta p\delta q$ are defined by the tables

C	1	2	3		E	1	2	3
*1	1	2	3		*1	1	2	3
2	1	1	1		2	2	1	2
3	1	1	1		3	3	2	1

$CEpqC\delta p\delta q$ is verified in this case, even if δ can be any 3-valued operator, for $Epq = 1$ only when p and q have the same value, so that $C\delta p\delta q$ will then have the value 1 also, while when $Epq \neq 1$ the whole $= 1$ because $C\overline{1}p = 1$ for any p. But these tables do not verify $CCpqCCqpEpq$, since $CC23CC32E23 = C1C12 = C12 = 2$.

The contrast with the Lewis systems and Ł at this point is also lessened by the fact that although the Lewis systems cannot contain a prototethic with the law $CEpqC\delta p\delta q$, some of them (S5 and S4; also T) do contain the *rule* that if $E\alpha\beta$ is a law we may infer $C\delta\alpha\delta\beta$, where $\delta\alpha$ is any function of α and $\delta\beta$ the same function of β. In these systems it would therefore make no difference if we adopted the Leśniewskian practice of expressing a definition '$\alpha = \beta$' as an axiomatic equivalence $E\alpha\beta$. ($E\alpha\beta$, if laid down as a law of one of these systems, would ensure interchangeability of α and β in all the contexts the system supplies.) And in all the Lewis systems, from S1 upwards, we have the weaker rule that if $E'\alpha\beta$ ('α is *strictly* equivalent to β', $NMNE\alpha\beta$) is a law, then α and β are interchangeable in all contexts;[1] so that in all these systems definitions could be expressed as laws of the form $E'\alpha\beta$, and they are in fact so expressed by Lewis. But in Q we have not even this. (In Q, for example, $E'pKpAqNq$ is a law but not $E'LpLKpAqNq$. For p might be always true when

---

[1] In T, S4, and S5, the stronger rule follows from this one because in these we have $\alpha \rightarrow NMN\alpha$, and so $E\alpha\beta \rightarrow E'\alpha\beta$.

KpAqNq is not always true but sometimes inexpressible through the inexpressibility of *q*.) Q is thus at this point even less like Ł, that is it is even less extensional, than the Lewis systems.[1]

These points give rise to two questions, namely (1) what system of propositional calculus with functorial variables *could* be taken up without modification into a system containing non-extensional operators of the category of δ? and (2) in what way could definitions be expressed as laws even in the system Q?[2] Both are simply answered. For (1) we need do no more than introduce variables of the category of δ with ordinary substitution rules, but with no special axioms, into the propositional calculus with *C* and Π undefined, with *CCpqrCCrpCsp* as sole axiom, with substitution, detachment, and Π1 and Π2 in the completely general form

$$\Pi 1 : C\alpha\beta \rightarrow C\Pi x\alpha\beta$$

$$\Pi 2 : C\alpha\beta \rightarrow C\alpha\Pi x\beta, \text{ for } x \text{ not free in } \alpha;$$

in which *x* may be a variable of any type which the system comes to contain. Łukasiewicz has shown[3] that the axiom *CCCpqrCCrpCsp* suffices, with substitution and detachment, for that part of the classical propositional calculus which uses no operator but *C*; it can easily be shown that the full propositional calculus is obtainable when we add to this the rules for quantifiers and the usual definitions of o, *N*, etc., in terms of *C* and Π (o = Πpp; *Np* = *Cp*o). When, however, functorial variables are introduced we cannot on this basis prove such formulae as *CEpqCδpδq* or *CδpCδNpδq*, though we can prove such formulae as

$$CK\delta q\delta N\gamma qNK\Pi pC\delta pp\Pi pC\delta p\gamma p,$$

in which δ and γ may stand not only for truth-operators but equally well for operators like 'It is possible that —', 'It will be the case that —', or even '*x* asserts that —' or '*x* does not know whether —'. The formula just given could, for example, stand for

> If the judge says on Monday that the prisoner will be hanged on Saturday (δq), and the judge also says on Monday that the prisoner will not know

[1] Mr. E. J. Lemmon has pointed out to me that there is not here a simple linear series with decreasing extensionality; for we do have in Q the rule to infer *C$\delta\alpha\delta\beta$* from the law *E$\alpha\beta$*, provided α and β have the same variables, and that we have this for *E* and not merely for *E'* is a point in common with the *more* extensional Lewis systems.

[2] These are analogous to the questions raised, though not quite answered, in Chapter VII, about the effects of introducing non-extensional operators into Leśniewski's ontology, with special reference to theses of extensionality and onto-logical definitions.

[3] 'The Shortest Axiom of the Implicational Calculus of Propositions', *Proceedings of the Royal Irish Academy*, 52 A 3 (1948).

on Saturday whether he will be hanged on Saturday ($\delta N\gamma q$), then it is not the case that both whatever the judge says on Monday is true ($\Pi p C\delta p p$) and whatever the judge says on Monday the prisoner will know on Saturday ($\Pi p C\delta p\gamma p$).

This prototetic has no special postulates associated with *variables* of the type of δ (over and above the rules of substitution and quantification which go with variables of any type at all); it has only an axiom (and a rule—detachment) associated with one of the *constants* of this category (the truth-functional C). Hence its laws concerning δ do not depend for their validity upon the poverty of the system, and we can introduce without trouble further constants (such as L and M) with their own special postulates.[1]

To the second question, the answer is that Łukasiewicz's method of expressing a definition '$\alpha = \beta$' as an axiom of the form $C\delta\alpha\delta\beta$[2] will ensure complete interchangeability of *definiens* and *definiendum* even in Q, provided that δ can stand for any monadic statement-forming operator on statements which the system in question contains.

One further comparison: Lp and Mp may be said to be *collapsed inwardly* if both are equated to p, and *collapsed outwardly* if Lp is equated with the contradictory function Fp and Mp with the tautological function Vp. The Lewis systems S1–5 all admit of inward collapsing by the addition of $CpLp$ or $CMpp$, but none admit of outward collapsing, since all contain theses beginning with L and with NM, so that the addition of NLp or of Mp would result in a contradiction. The Lewis systems S6–8 admit neither of outward collapsing (for the same reason as the others) nor of inward (since they contain the thesis MMp, which with $CMpp$ would yield first Mp and then the plain p). The Ł-modal system, apart from the rejections, admits both of inward collapsing by adding $CMpp$ and of outward collapsing by adding Mp, though not of both simultaneously. Q admits both of the outward collapsing of L and NLN by adding NLp (since, like Ł, it has no theses beginning with L), and of the inward collapsing of M and NMN by adding $CMpp$; and these two collapses are possible both separately and simultaneously. (This has been pointed out to me by Mr. E. J. Lemmon who has studied the resulting systems in some detail.) Q also admits of the inward collapsing of L and NLN by adding $CpLp$, and this

---

[1] There already existed in 1923, in Tarski's doctoral dissertation (now available in English as the first item in his *Logic, Semantics and Metamathematics*, translated by J. H. Woodger), a brilliant study of the differences between a prototetic with the law of extensionality (which Tarski calls the 'law of substitution') and one without it.

[2] 'On Variable Functors of Propositional Arguments', *Proceedings of the Royal Irish Academy*, 54 A 2 (1951). Cf. my *Formal Logic*, p. 97.

entails the simultaneous inward collapse of M and NMN; but it does not admit of the outward collapsing of M and NMN by adding Mp, since it contains laws beginning with NM. The L of Q being thus collapsible both ways, the theses of Q which contain L but not M must all be theses of the Ł-modal system, since this contains all formulae in which Lp may be equally well interpreted as Fp or as P.

The System A

THERE are some modal logicians who feel that statements containing sequences of modal operators like *MM*, *MML*, and so on are one and all 'meaningless'. (This is clearly what an adherent of the Quine–Smart view would hold about sequences of tense-operators.) My own worries about the common modal systems are rather different from this, but the formal properties of a calculus enshrining this viewpoint are worth studying, and so far as I know have not been studied hitherto.

Suppose we introduce two different types of propositional variables—say *a*, *b*, *c*, etc., which we may call A-variables, and *p*, *q*, *r*, etc., which we may call P-variables. The following, and the following only, are to be counted as A-formulae, and are substitutable in theses for A-variables:

  (i) All A-variables.

 (ii) *N*α, where α is any A-formula.

(iii) *K*αβ, *C*αβ, *A*αβ, *E*αβ, where α and β are both P-formulae and at least one of them is an A-formula.

And the following, and the following only, are to be counted as P-formulae, and are substitutable in theses for P-variables:

  (i) All P-variables.

 (ii) *N*α, where α is any P-formula.

(iii) *K*αβ, *C*αβ, *A*αβ, *E*αβ, where α and β are any P-formulae.

(iv) All A-formulae.

 (v) *M*α and *L*α, where α is any A-formula.

If α is an A-formula, it should be observed, *M*α and *L*α are P-formulae, but they are not A-formulae, so that *MM*α, *ML*α, *LM*α, and *LL*α are not even P-formulae, since *M*α and *L*α are only P-formulae where α is an A-formula. Longer sequences of *M*'s and *L*'s are similarly excluded. And in a system of this type we cannot deduce, say, *CLLaLa* by substitution in *CLaa*, since *La*, not being an A-formula, is not substitutable for the A-variable *a*.

The number of non-equivalent modalities in any such system is clearly 6, as in S5 and Ł; this is, indeed, not merely the number of non-equivalent modalities but, quite absolutely, the number of modalities. Other features of the system depend on how it is axiomatized. Before suggesting an axiomatization, it should be noted that we can prove in S5 a number of formulae which do not contain sequences of modal operators (and so would continue to be well formed in A, if these p's, q's, etc., were replaced by a's, b's, etc.) but which are not provable in weaker Lewis systems. For example, the formulae $CLCpLqLCMpq$, $CLCMpqLCpLq$, $CLCpLqCMpLq$, and $CLCMpqCMpLq$. These are all falsified by the 4-valued matrix given in our Chapter II, which is satisfied by all formulae of S4 but not by the distinctive formulae ($CMLpLp$, etc.) of S5. And in axiomatizing our System A, we need to decide whether we wish to include such formulae or not.

If we do wish to include them, I think we can do so by subjoining to the propositional calculus the definition of M as NLN and the following modification of my rules L1 and L2:

LA1: $C\alpha\beta{\rightarrow}CL\alpha\beta$, if α is an A-formula.

LA2: $C\alpha\beta{\rightarrow}C\alpha L\beta$, if β is an A-formula and there are no unmodalized variables in α.

We can at all events prove with these rules the analogues of the four formulae mentioned above. For example, we can prove $CLCaLbC\text{-}MaLb$ as follows:

$CCaLbCNLbNa$ (substitution in $CCpqCNqNp$)

${\rightarrow}CLCaLbCNLbNa$ (LA1)

${\rightarrow}CKLCaLbNLbNa$ (substitution in $CCpCqrCKpqr$)

${\rightarrow}CKLCaLbNLbLNa$ (LA2)

${\rightarrow}CLCaLbCNLbLNa$ (substitution in $CCKpqrCpCqr$)

${\rightarrow}CLCaLbCNLNaLb$ ($CCNpqCNqp$, $CCpqCCqrCpr$)

${\rightarrow}CLCaLbCMaLb$ (Df. M).

The following would seem to be a characteristic matrix for the system: Let A-variables take as possible values infinite sequences of 2's and 3's, and P-variables take these and also infinite sequences of 1's and 4's, and let the sequence consisting entirely of 1's and that consisting entirely of 2's both be designated sequences, and the only designated sequences. Let C, A, and E be defined in terms of N and K in the usual way, and the sequences for Np and Kpq be determined as follows:

$$N(xyz \ldots) = (Nx)(Ny)(Nz) \ldots$$
$$K(xyz \ldots)(x'y'z' \ldots) = (Kxx')(Kyy')(Kzz') \ldots$$

the values with N attached to a single figure and K to two single figures being given by the tables

K	1	2	3	4	N
1	1	2	3	4	4
2	2	2	3	3	3
3	3	3	3	3	2
4	4	3	3	4	1

It will be seen that N turns a 1–4 sequence into a 1–4 sequence and a 2–3 sequence into a 2–3 sequence, while K turns all pairs of sequences into 2–3 sequences except where both members of the pair are 1–4 sequences. M and L attach only to variables having 2–3 sequences for their values; and if the sequence for a has any 2's in it, the sequence for Ma is that consisting of 1's only, while if the sequence for a consists entirely of 3's, that for Ma consists entirely of 4's. Interchange 2's and 3's, and 1's and 4's, in this description of the conditions for M, and we have the conditions for L. Given this infinite characteristic matrix for A, it can be shown by Dugundji's method that it has no finite characteristic matrix.

An alternative axiomatization would of course be the definition of L as NMN and an analogous modification of my rules M1 and M2. The point is worth making because Mr. E. J. Lemmon has suggested to me that that fragment of Q—call it QM—which does not contain Q's distinctive L, may be axiomatized by subjoining to the propositional calculus the rules M2 ($C\alpha\beta\rightarrow C\alpha M\beta$) and a different modification of M1, namely

QM1: $C\alpha\beta\rightarrow CM\alpha\beta$, provided that all propositional variables in β are modalized, and occur in α.

If this conjecture is correct, we may exhibit the relations between some of the main systems considered here in the following way. Suppose we use the abbreviations

CPC for the classical propositional calculus,
IPC for the intuitionist propositional calculus,
Prot for prototethic with the axiom $C\delta pC\delta Np\delta q$,
BML ('basic modal logic') for CPC+M2,
IBML for IPC+M2,
ABML for CPC+AM2,
MI for IBML+M1,

and consider only systems in which L occurs, if at all, as a mere abbreviation for NMN. (That is, we omit Q, and omit the full MIPC of Chapter IV, in which IPC is supplemented by L1 and L2 as well as M1 and M2.) Then we have (1) three non-modal systems CPC, IPC and Prot; (2) four 'basic' modal systems derived by adding M2 or a modification to one of the preceding—BML, IBML, ABML, and Ł ($= $ Prot$+$M2); and (3) four 'enriched' modal systems derived by adding M1 or a modification to the preceding—MI, A ($=$ ABML$+$AM1), QM ($=$ BML$+$QM1) and S5 (BML$+$M1). If we use 'Ext' for the law of extensionality $CEpqC\delta p\delta q$ and 'AP' for the formation rule 'All P-formulae are A-formulae', we also have these equivalences: Prot $=$ CPC$+$Ext, so that Ł $=$ BML$+$Ext; and S5 $=$ A$+$AP.

It is of some significance that Ł is a 'basic' modal system by our criterion; though (a) it is too strong to tolerate 'enrichment' by M1 or either of our modifications of it, and (b) it is the only basic modal system, in our sense, in which the equivalence of NLN and M is provable from the definition of L as NMN. In ABML and BML we may proceed thus far: $NLN = NNMNN = MNN$, but no farther; but in Ł we may obtain $EMNNpMp$ from $ENNpp$ and $CEpqC\delta p\delta q$. (The latter of course amounts to a new modal postulate when M is added to the operators substitutable for δ, so that in a sense Ł has a further modal postulate beside M2 and is thus far 'enriched' rather than 'basic'.)

This result—the proof of Łukasiewicz's basic modal logic in its entirety, including $ENLNpMp$—can of course be achieved by making a less powerful addition to the BML of our table, namely by just adding $EMNNpMp$ directly (or, for that matter, by directly adding $ENLNpMp$, i.e. $ENNMNNpMp$, but since we already have $ENNpp$ in CPC, this effects no more and no less than the other). Łukasiewicz in fact gives his own basic modal logic this axiomatic form before enlarging it to Ł. But there is a more interesting way of achieving something very similar.

It is clear that variants of our system A may be constructed by having somewhat more restrictive rules for the formation of A-formulae. Instead of our rule that if α and β are P-formulae and at least one of them is an A-formula, then $C\alpha\beta$, etc., are A-formulae, we might rule that C, etc., are A-formulae if and only if *both* α and β are A-formulae. Even with AM1 and AM2 still used as our special postulates, this new formation-rule would seem to make formulae which are in S5 but not in any weaker Lewis system no longer provable. Certainly we shall no longer have $CLCaLbCMaLb$, etc., for the antecedents of this group are not well formed by the new criterion ($LCaLb$ is not a P-formula because $CaLb$ is not now an

A-formula). And there will be no theses with an L for their first symbol except ones in which what L is prefixed to is a formula of the propositional calculus. (We will have, for example, $LCaa$; but not, say, $LCaMa$.)

A still stricter system is obtainable if we admit as A-formulae only A-variables and the negations of A-formulae; and in this case the addition of Df. L, AM1, and AM2 to the propositional calculus will yield only those formulae which could equally be obtained by adding AM2 (or $CaMa$) and $EMNNaMa$. This last equivalence is derivable as follows:

1. $CNNpp$
   $1p/a \text{ AM2} = 2$

2. $CNNaMa$
   $2 \times \text{AM1} = 3$

3. $CMNNaMa,$

and the converse implication similarly, using $CpNNp$. This and trivial variants of it (such as $EMNNNaMNA$) are all we can derive using these rules; to pass from, e.g., $CaAab$ to $CMaMAab$, or from $CKaba$ to $CMKabMa$, would be to introduce ill-formed elements, and to violate the condition that the formula to which the new M is prefixed must be an A-formula. In this case, therefore, the enriched modal logic, in our sense of 'enriched', is simply the basic modal logic, in Łukasiewicz's sense of 'basic'. Using A′ and A″ for our two modifications of A, we might say that what is formalized in A″ is simply the traditional theory of modal opposition (including subalternation, and the *consequentiae ab esse ad posse* and *a necesse esse ad esse*) and equipollence, which is what Łukasiewicz's 'basic modal logic' summarizes.

The relation of A″ to Łukasiewicz's Ł contrasts sharply with that of our other 'enriched' systems; since with its proviso interpreted by the formation rules of A″, the rule AM1 is so far from 'de-modalizing' Ł (making it possible to prove $CMpp$) that it yields nothing that Ł does not already contain—it gives us nothing that is not given by simply shifting the 'non-modal' basis from CPC to (extensional) protothetic, and not as much as that. A″ does indeed contain the rule 'Infer $NMN\alpha$ from α, provided that α be modalizable'; but this—which would otherwise work havoc with Ł—is a rule without application, since no thesis ever *is* modalizable in A″. (The only modalizable forms are single variables with or without a preceding sequence of N's, and none of these are theses.)

Infinite matrices characteristic for A′ and A″ are obtained by taking that already given for A itself and replacing the tables for deriving the figure at any given place in a Kpq sequence from the figures at that place in p and q sequences, by the following variants:

K	1	2	3	4			K	1	2	3	4	
							1	1	1	4	4	
A′ 1	1	1	4	4			2	1	1	4	4	A″
2	1	2	3	4			3	4	4	4	4	
3	4	3	3	4			4	4	4	4	4	
4	4	4	4	4								

With A′ a proof along Dugundji's lines that there is no finite characteristic matrix is still available; but with A″ it is not, as Dugundji's proof involves the form $E'ab$, i.e. $NMNEab$, and in A″ this is ill formed ($NEab$ not being an A-formula, $MNEab$ and $NMNEab$ are not P-formulae).

In fact A″, like Ł, has a finite characteristic matrix, namely the following 6-valued one (A-variables taking the values 2–5 only):

K	1	2	3	4	5	6	N	M
*1	1	1	1	6	6	6	6	—
*2	1	1	1	6	6	6	5	1
3	1	1	1	6	6	6	4	1
4	6	6	6	6	6	6	3	1
5	6	6	6	6	6	6	2	6
6	6	6	6	6	6	6	1	—

(The value 2 is designated vacuously, since the only formulae which have this value are isolated variables or the same preceded by sequences of N's, and all these take other values also, and so are not made laws by the designation. 3 might have been vacuously designated also.) Intuitively, p may here be thought of as having the value

    1 if it is true and unmodalizable,
    2 if it is true and necessary,
    3 if it is true and contingent,
    4 if it is false and contingent,
    5 if it is false and impossible,
    6 if it is false and unmodalizable.

The values, in this sense, of all formulae in the present system are determined when the values of their variables are. Functions about which we might be doubtful on intuitive grounds—e.g. $MKab$, which might be false and might be true with a contingently false and *b* contingently true—just do not occur in the system. The matrix verifies all the postulates; and conversely, all theses assumed in calculating with the tables appear to be demonstrable in the system; for example the formula

$$E(Ma)AA(KaNMNa)(KaMNa)(KNaMa),$$

asserting in effect that $Ma = 1$ if and only if $a = 2$ or 3 or 4; and

$$E(KNaNMNNa)(KNaNMa),$$

asserting in effect that $Na = 2$ (is true and necessary) if and only if $a = 5$ (is false and impossible).

If we admit no A-formulae but A-variables, AM1 becomes redundant (so that the 'basic' and 'enriched' systems coincide), and Df. *L* fails to give us not only $ENLNaMa$ but even $ENMNaLa$, since in this system (call it A‴) $NMNa$ is ill-formed. A‴ has the following 5-valued characteristic matrix (with A-variables taking the values 2, 3, and 4 only):

K	1	2	3	4	5	N	M
*1	1	1	5	5	5	5	—
2	1	1	5	5	5	5	1
3	5	5	5	5	5	1	1
4	5	5	5	5	5	1	5
5	5	5	5	5	5	1	—

Here $a = 2$ if and only if $KaMa$, 3 if and only if $KNaMa$, and 4 if and only if $KNaNMa$; the first case no longer having, as in A″, the sub-possibilities $KaNMNa$ and $KaMNa$.

At the other end of the A-series, in between A and S5, we could have a system in which to the formation-rules of A we add 'If α is an A-formula so are $M\alpha$ and $L\alpha$', but still do not permit the prefixing of M and L to P-variables or to formulae containing only P-variables. In the infinite matrix characteristic for this sequence, the N–K transformations would be as in A, and M would still attach only to 2–3 sequences, but the result of such modalizing would also be a 2–3 sequence (not a 1–4 one, as in A). Iterated modalities would occur in this system, with laws as in S5, so that the two kinds of variable might well seem a superfluous complication; but the system would be of use in tense-logic to those who hold that there are *both* tensed and tenseless propositions, such forms as 'It is, has been, or will be the case that p' being without sense when p is tenseless, but p being tensed if it has any tensed component.

The above system, and A and A', admit of inward but not of outward collapsing (like S1–5; see previous Appendix); while A″ and A‴, like Ł without the rejections, admit of both.

APPENDIX D

Modal and Deontic Logic

It was suggested in a recent paper by Dr. Alan Ross Anderson[1] that deontic logic, i.e. the logic of obligation, permissibility, etc., may be systematized by introducing into some ordinary modal system a propositional constant $\mathscr{P}$, adding as the sole extra axiom the assertion that $\mathscr{P}$ is contingent (i.e. $KM\mathscr{P}MN\mathscr{P}$), and defining the deontic operators in terms of M and $\mathscr{P}$. $\mathscr{P}$ may be read as 'The world will be worse off', 'Punishment ought to follow', or something of that sort, and 'p is permissible' defined as 'It is possible for p to occur without $\mathscr{P}$', 'p is forbidden' as 'p strictly implies $\mathscr{P}$', and 'p is obligatory' as 'The omission of p strictly implies $\mathscr{P}$'; or in symbols (using Pp for 'p is permissible', Fp for 'p is forbidden' and Op for 'p is obligatory'):

$$\text{Df. } P: \quad Pp = MKpN\mathscr{P}.$$

$$\text{Df. } F: \quad Fp = NPp = NMKpN\mathscr{P} = C'p\mathscr{P}.$$

$$\text{Df. } O: \quad Op = FNp = NMKNpN\mathscr{P} = C'Np\mathscr{P}.$$

(Anderson suggests more complex definitions, but these will do for our present purpose.) On this basis, Anderson has pointed out, it is possible to demonstrate, for example, all of the laws in von Wright's deontic logic,[2] and also the law $OCOpp$ ('It is obligatory that what is obligatory be done'), on which I have written elsewhere.[3]

Indeed, with the above definitions we may obtain all these results, in most modal systems, with the plain $MN\mathscr{P}$ as our sole special axiom. In other words, while the standard systems of deontic logic require that 'the bad thing' ($\mathscr{P}$) should not be necessary, they are compatible with its being impossible, i.e. with everything that is possible being permissible. This is just another way of saying that deontic logic has the formal structure of a fragment of ordinary modal logic, with P for M and O for L; and it may be collapsed into a plain modal system by adding as a thesis the formula $CMpPp$.

---

[1] A. R. Anderson, *The Formal Analysis of Normative Concepts*, Technical Report No. 2, U.S. Office of Naval Research Contract No. SAR/Nonr–609 (16), 1956.

[2] G. H. von Wright, *An Essay in Modal Logic*, ch. v.

[3] A. N. Prior, *Formal Logic*, pp. 225–6; 'A Note on the Logic of Obligation', *Revue Philosophique de Louvain*, Feb. 1956.

This formula is deductively equivalent to $NM\mathscr{P}$, for

(1) $CM p P p$

→ (2) $CM p M K p N\mathscr{P}$ (Df. P)

→ (3) $CM\mathscr{P} M K\mathscr{P} N\mathscr{P}$ ((2) $p/\mathscr{P}$)

→ (4) $NM\mathscr{P}$ ($NMK p N p$ and (3))

and

(4) $NM\mathscr{P}$

→ (5) $NMK p\mathscr{P}$

→ (6) $CM p NMK p\mathscr{P}$ ($C p C q p$)

→ (2) $CM p M K p N\mathscr{P}$ (from (6) and $CM p AMK p q MK p N q$)

→ (1) $CM p P p$ (Df. P).

The $M\mathscr{P}$ in Anderson's axiom blocks this extension of deontic logic, but in most systems it does not seem to lead to any new positive theses of a strictly deontic character, i.e. theses in which $\mathscr{P}$ only occurs as an implicit part of a formula in P, O, or F. (In systems with quantifiers it would lead to such further formulae as $\Sigma p K M p N P p$, 'Something is possible without being permissible'.)

The simple $MN\mathscr{P}$, it may be further noted, is deductively equivalent in most modal systems to $CO p P p$, 'What is obligatory is permissible'. For we may prove $CO p P p$ from $MN\mathscr{P}$ as follows:

(7) $CqAKN p q K p q$

→ (8) $CM q M A K N p q K p q$ ($C\alpha\beta \to CM\alpha M\beta$)

→ (9) $CM q A M K N p q M K p q$ ($MA p q = AM p M q$)

→ (10) $CM q C N M K N p q M K p q$ ($A = CN$)

→ (11) $CMN\mathscr{P} C N M K N p N\mathscr{P} M K p N\mathscr{P}$ ((10) $q/N\mathscr{P}$)

→ (12) $CMN\mathscr{P} C O p P p$ (Dff. O, P)

→ (13) $CO p P p$ ($MN\mathscr{P}$ and (12)),

while the converse deduction may be performed as follows:

(14) $CN p M N\mathscr{P}$ ($CMK p q M q$ with $p/N p$, $q/N\mathscr{P}$, and Df. P)

(15) $CP p M N\mathscr{P}$ ($CMK p q M q$ with $q/N\mathscr{P}$, and Df. P)

(16) $CN P N p P p$ ($CO p P p$ and $O = N P N$)

→ (17) $AP N p P p$ ($A = CN$)

∴ (18) $MN\mathscr{P}$ ((14), (15), (17) and $CC p r CC q r CA p q r$).

Whether we use Anderson's axiom, the plain $MN\mathscr{P}$ or $CO p P p$ as our sole axiom, the definition of P, O, and F in terms of M and $\mathscr{P}$

makes possible a quite remarkable simplification of the postulates of deontic logic.

But it does more than this. It also gives us new means of investigating the relations of deontic logic and ordinary modal logic. Thus, given (13) and Df. P, it is a simple matter to prove the Kantian principle that what is obligatory must be possible. For

$$(19)\quad CMKpN\mathcal{P}Mp\ (CMKpqMp\ \text{with}\ q/N\mathcal{P})$$

$$\rightarrow (20)\quad CPpMp\ (\text{Df.}\ P)$$

$$\rightarrow (21)\quad COpMp\ ((13)\ \text{and}\ (20)).$$

And we can set about answering more subtle questions in this field. For example, Mr. P. T. Geach has suggested that intuitively the assertion that it is permissible that there should be someone ϕ-ing $(P\Sigma x\phi x)$ is weaker than the assertion that there *is* someone to whom it is permissible to ϕ $(\Sigma xP\phi x)$, but equivalent to the assertion that there *could be* someone to whom it is permissible to ϕ $(M\Sigma xP\phi x)$. Using the above definitions with different quantified modal systems, in what system or systems would we have $C\Sigma xP\phi xP\Sigma x\phi x$ but not its converse, and both $CM\Sigma xP\phi xP\Sigma x\phi x$ and its converse? Let us use

(a) for $P\Sigma x\phi x$, i.e. $MK\Sigma x\phi xN\mathcal{P}$,

(b) for $\Sigma xP\phi x$, i.e. $\Sigma xMK\phi xN\mathcal{P}$,

(c) for $M\Sigma xP\phi x$, i.e. $M\Sigma xMK\phi xN\mathcal{P}$.

Then some natural ways of proving $C(a)(b)$, $C(b)(a)$, $C(a)(c)$, and $C(c)(a)$ would be the following:

$(22)\quad CK\Sigma x\phi xN\mathcal{P}\Sigma xK\phi xN\mathcal{P}$ (from quantification theory)

$(23)\quad CMK\Sigma x\phi xN\mathcal{P}M\Sigma xK\phi xN\mathcal{P}$ $(C\alpha\beta \rightarrow CM\alpha M\beta)$

$(24)\quad CMK\Sigma x\phi xN\mathcal{P}\Sigma xMK\phi xN\mathcal{P}$ $(M\Sigma x \rightarrow \Sigma xM$, by the Barcan formula)

$\quad\quad = C(a)(b)$

$(25)\quad C\Sigma xK\phi xN\mathcal{P}K\Sigma x\phi xN\mathcal{P}$ (from quantification theory)

$(26)\quad CM\Sigma xK\phi xN\mathcal{P}MK\Sigma x\phi xN\mathcal{P}$ $(C\alpha\beta \rightarrow CM\alpha M\beta)$

$(27)\quad C\Sigma xMK\phi xN\mathcal{P}MK\Sigma x\phi xN\mathcal{P}$ $(\Sigma xM \rightarrow M\Sigma x$, converse of B.f.)

$\quad\quad = C(b)(a)$

$(28)\quad C\Sigma xK\phi xN\mathcal{P}\Sigma xMK\phi xN\mathcal{P}$ $(CpMp, \Sigma 1, \Sigma 2)$

$(29)\quad CM\Sigma xK\phi xN\mathcal{P}M\Sigma xMK\phi xN\mathcal{P}$ $(C\alpha\beta \rightarrow CM\alpha M\beta)$

$(30)\quad CMK\Sigma x\phi xN\mathcal{P}M\Sigma xMK\phi xN\mathcal{P}$ (from (23) and (29))

$\quad\quad = C(a)(c)$

$(31)\quad C\Sigma xMK\phi xN\mathcal{P}M\Sigma xK\phi xN\mathcal{P}$ (converse of B.f.)

(32) $CM\Sigma xMK\phi x N\mathscr{P}MM\Sigma xK\phi x N\mathscr{P}$ $(C\alpha\beta \rightarrow CM\alpha M\beta)$

(33) $CM\Sigma xMK\phi x N\mathscr{P}M\Sigma xK\phi x N\mathscr{P}$ $(CMMpMp)$

(34) $CM\Sigma xMK\phi x N\mathscr{P}MK\Sigma x\phi x N\mathscr{P}$ (from (33) and (26))

$= C(c)(a)$.

All of the rules and theses employed in these proofs are available in Q, with the exception of the Barcan formula (the proviso in Q upon the inference of $CM\alpha M\beta$ from $C\alpha\beta$ is met wherever the rule is here used). The Barcan formula is used only in the proof of $C(a)(b)$, so Q appears to have the properties which Geach requires, i.e. non-provability of $C(a)(b)$ and provability of all the rest. In S5 all four proofs can be carried out; but the first implication probably cannot be proved in weaker Lewis systems unless the Barcan formula is added as a special axiom, and the last probably not in systems not containing $CMMpMp$.

It must be added, however, that if Q is used as our modal basis some very simple and obvious deontic laws cease to be derivable from $MN\mathscr{P}$ or even from $KM\mathscr{P}MN\mathscr{P}$. For example, (13) and (21), i.e. $COpPp$ and $COpMp$. Our proof of (21) from (19), (13), and Df. P could indeed be carried out in Q if (13) were given, but our proof of (13) from (7) and $MN\mathscr{P}$ fails, for in the step from (7) to (8) the condition attached in Q to the deducibility of $CM\alpha M\beta$ from $C\alpha\beta$ is not met. As far as the matrix is concerned, whether (13) and (21) will ever take undesignated values will depend on what value is assigned to the constant $\mathscr{P}$. The axiom $MN\mathscr{P}$ would restrict our choice here to sequences containing 3's, and Anderson's full axiom would restrict it further to sequences containing both 1's and 3's, but even the stricter condition leaves it open to us to choose a sequence for $\mathscr{P}$ which, with certain p's, will contain 1's wherever p has 1's or 3's, and 3's only where p has 2's. For example, $\mathscr{P}$ might (while being true in some possible states of affairs and false in others, and so satisfying Anderson's axiom) be false only in possible states of affairs in which I do not exist, and true in all in which I do, so that in no possible circumstances will any act or omission of mine be unaccompanied by 'the bad thing'. 'The bad thing' will thus—although contingent—be entailed by whatever I do or fail to do, in fact by my very existence, so that whatever I do will be forbidden, and yet it will be obligatory also, since its omission will be also forbidden. And even impossible things, i.e. things which I cannot but omit, will be obligatory (their omission will be forbidden). The possibility of developing Q in this rather sombre and hyper-Calvinistic direction is perhaps already foreshadowed (though not yet realized) in its accordance with Geach's metatheorem, with its suggestion that perhaps no existing individuals are permitted to do a certain thing, though there might in a different state of affairs have been individuals who were. In any case it is clear that to obtain (13) and (21) in Q it is necessary to characterize $\mathscr{P}$ more explicitly by using a stronger axiom, say (13) itself, which will in effect place further restrictions on the values assignable to this constant. So far as I can see, to verify (13) by the matrix the sequence assigned to $\mathscr{P}$ will need to have a 3 in the first place, since it is possible to assign to a variable p a sequence with 2's in all places but the first, and with a 1 in this place for $\mathscr{P}$, both $MKpN\mathscr{P}$ (Pp) and $MKNpN\mathscr{P}$ (PNp) will be false in the only circumstance in which they are statable. However, there are probably other (less direct) ways of constructing a characteristic matrix for Q+(13).

On the other hand, there is no difficulty in Q about the proof of the law $OCOpp$, this being provable even in Q with nothing added but the definition of O, thus:

(35) $NMKNMpp$ (provable in Q)

→ (36) $NMKNMKNpN\mathscr{P}KNpN\mathscr{P}$ ((35) $p/KNpN\mathscr{P}$)

→ (37) $NMKOpKNpN\mathscr{P}$ (Df. O)

→ (38) $NMKKOpNpN\mathscr{P}$ ($KpKqr = KKpqr$)

→ (39) $NMKNNKOpNpN\mathscr{P}$ ($NNp = p$)

→ (40) $NMKNCOppN\mathscr{P}$ ($NKpNq = Cpq$)

→ (41) $OCOpp$ (Df. O).

Another modal system in which we might expect to obtain odd results if it is used as a basis for an Andersonian deontic logic is Ł. We do in fact obtain such results, but not as many as might have been anticipated. In the first place, since Ł contains the law $CKMpMNpMq$, the addition of $KM\mathscr{P}MN\mathscr{P}$ would at once make everything whatever possible (or to put it differently, the rejection of Mp as a thesis leads by $CKMpMNpMq$ to the rejection of $KM\mathscr{P}MN\mathscr{P}$ as a thesis). However, there is no objection to adding the plain $MN\mathscr{P}$, and if we do so all of von Wright's formulae, and the Kantian law $COpMp$, are provable in Ł as in other systems. However, we cannot prove $OCOpp$, or anything else beginning with O, since there cannot be theses in Ł beginning with NM (and this, of course, is why our proof of $OCOpp$ from proposition (35) above cannot be carried out, for that proposition, $NMKNMpp$, is not available in Ł). There are also intuitively peculiar deontic propositions provable in Ł from some of its intuitively peculiar modal theorems, e.g. from its law $CKMpMqMKpq$ we can prove $CKPpPqPKpq$.

If the modal system used is A, the results obtained depend on whether the propositional constant $\mathscr{P}$ is counted as an A-formula or not. If it is, such forms as PPa will be allowable; if not, not. For $PPa = MKPaN\mathscr{P} = MKMKaN\mathscr{P}N\mathscr{P}$; and if $\mathscr{P}$ is an A-formula, $N\mathscr{P}$ is an A-formula, and $KMKaN\mathscr{P}N\mathscr{P}$ is an A-formula, capable of having an M prefixed, so that the whole is well formed. But if $\mathscr{P}$ is not an A-formula, $N\mathscr{P}$ is not, and $KMKaN\mathscr{P}N\mathscr{P}$ is not either (since its other component $MKaN\mathscr{P}$ is certainly not one), and so cannot have the M prefixed to form PPa. $OCOaa$ is well formed, and provable, on both rulings; $COaPa$ and $COaMa$ are also well formed on both rulings, but not provable by Anderson's method if $\mathscr{P}$ is not an A-formula, since in that case $KM\mathscr{P}MN\mathscr{P}$ cannot be laid down as an axiom, being ill formed. Nor can even $MN\mathscr{P}$ on its own be laid down, for the same reason. It is not that $\mathscr{P}$ becomes under these conditions a necessary proposition; it is simply unmodalizable; and $COaPa$ and $COaMa$ can be brought into the system easily enough by laying down the former as sole axiom. And as in most other systems, all of von Wright's laws will be provable on this basis. But one formula which becomes unprovable, because unformulable, under these conditions, is $F\mathscr{P}$ (i.e. $NMK\mathscr{P}N\mathscr{P}$), asserting that 'the bad thing' is itself forbidden. Whether or not this is a desirable feature depends, I suppose, on whether or not morality is to be thought of as having a foundation beyond itself.

In A', neither PPa nor $OCOaa$ is well formed even if $\mathscr{P}$ is an A-formula; and unless it is one, Pa, Oa, and Fa are not well formed either. But given the favourable formation-rule, all of von Wright's deontic laws, and also $COaMa$ and $F\mathscr{P}$, are provable in A' from Anderson's axiom, and it is of some interest that so weak a modal system suffices for this. But in A″ and A‴ the forms Pa, Oa, and Fa are quite ruled out; though if $\mathscr{P}$ is an A-formula the axiom $KM\mathscr{P}MN\mathscr{P}$ is well formed in A″. In A‴ even the plain $MN\mathscr{P}$ is ill formed.

INDEX

PRINTED IN GREAT BRITAIN
AT THE UNIVERSITY PRESS, OXFORD
BY CHARLES BATEY, PRINTER TO THE UNIVERSITY